ABOUT TH

Barbara Comyns was born in 1909, the daughter of an increasingly unsuccessful Birmingham brewer, and was brought up on a Warwickshire country estate with her five siblings. They had little formal education and were largely educated by governesses, who allowed them to run wild.

Barbara started writing when she was 10 and always illustrated her work. In her teens she studied at Hatherley's Art School in London before finding a job drawing cartoons in an animation studio. She married an artist, John Pemberton, in 1931 and lived in bohemian poverty. They had two children before the relationship ended in 1935, when Barbara supported her family with modelling, running an antique business and dealing in vintage cars. She was a talented painter who exhibited with the London Group and always thought of herself as more of an artist than a writer.

During the Second World War she lived with a black marketeer, before working in a Herefordshire country house as a cook to escape the Blitz. She wrote her first novel, *Sisters by a River*, at this time. It was published in 1947, a depiction of her childhood among large houses, servants and governesses. She followed it with *Our Spoons Came from Woolworths* and *Who Was Changed and Who Was Dead*. *The Vet's Daughter* was published in 1959 and became her most successful novel, serialised on BBC radio, adapted into a play and then into a musical.

Graham Greene, an early admirer of her writing, introduced Barbara to Richard Carr, a civil servant at the Foreign Office (and grandson of a playwright), they married in 1945. The couple honeymooned in Kim Philby's country cottage on Snowdonia.

Richard Carr later lost his job when Kim Philby was exposed as a spy and the family emigrated to Barcelona in the late 1950s. They spent nearly twenty years in Spain where Richard worked as a translator and Barbara continued to write.

They returned to London in 1974 and lived in the respectable suburbs of Twickenham and Richmond. Virago republished several of Barbara's early novels in the early 1980s while she published *The Juniper Tree* in 1985. Her final novel, *The House of Dolls*, appeared in 1989.

Barbara Comyns died in 1992.

MR FOX

BARBARA COMYNS

turnpike books

First published in Britain by Methuen London, Ltd, 1987

This paperback edition published 2020 by Turnpike Books

turnpikebooks@gmail.com

Reprinted 2021, 2022

ISBN 9781916254725

Printed and bound in Great Britain by Clays Ltd, Elcograf S.p.A.

Mr Fox

CHAPTER ONE

The other people in the house where I lived didn't like me. I expect it was because I was living with a man I wasn't married to. We just had 'Mr Fox and Mrs Caroline Seymore' written on the door that led to our flat. There was a Miss Seymore living there, too, but she didn't have her name on the door because she was only three years old. It wasn't very nice living in that attic flat in the house where the people didn't like us. When I came downstairs into the main hall, the middle-aged woman would open her door and sing a little song about 'nice people' with great emphasis on the 'nice', and when I had to go to the dustbins at the side of the house she would shut the door after me and however much I rang and knocked she wouldn't let me in. Sometimes I would call Jenny and she would climb down the stairs and let me in, but often I had to wait until Mr Fox came home, and he would be angry and say I should always remember to carry the front-door key. Once when we reached the flat we discovered Jenny cutting his shaving-brush into a sharp point. She said she was making it tidy, but Mr Fox wasn't pleased.

We often did things that made him displeased with us, but we had nowhere else to go, so we had to go on living with him.

Until quite recently I used to own a leasehold house. I lived in the semi-basement with Jenny and let the rest of the house in flats. The tenants were rather a bore – they were always complaining about each other and getting their sinks blocked up, but they were quite profitable and when they grumbled too much I used to give them a month's notice, and although they never went at the end of the month, it did them a lot of good. They became quite human for a few weeks.

Then everyone began to say there was going to be a war and instead of me giving the tenants notice, they gave it to me. One by one they left and the house became huge and empty and almost every day on the hall mat I would find demands for the rates and light and property tax and water and hire of gas cookers; all the time these beastly demands kept coming. They were all colours – pink, buff, blue, and each one more threatening than the last. Then men in bowler hats started coming, so I thought I'd better go.

I'd only got twenty-five pounds in the bank which was hardly worth dividing among the bowler-hatted men, and I decided I'd keep it myself to start a new life with. Twenty-five pounds wouldn't go very far, so I went to see Mr Fox to ask his advice. He had a garage in the neighbourhood where he used to sell sports cars; sometimes he used to buy cars for almost nothing that had been in crashes and he would patch them up and respray them so they looked like new and sell them at a great profit. He was always full of new ideas about making money and was often very prosperous, but sometimes almost penniless. But just when you thought, 'Now he really is ruined,' he would have another brainwave and make some more money. I expect he was rather dishonest really. Besides having a garage, Mr Fox owned a fine red beard, a pointed one. Sometimes when he had a lot of creditors and people hounding him he used to cut it off and look completely different, but not so nice.

I had known Mr Fox for about two years. At one time he owned some houses in the same road where I lived and we had first met over some business to do with one of his ex-tenants who had become a tenant of mine. Then we had become friends and I would look after his dog when he went away and in exchange he helped me with minor repairs in my house. It wasn't always holidays Mr Fox was enjoying when he went away. Sometimes he went to prison, not for crime but because he didn't pay his rates to the borough council. He thought it a pity to waste money on rates and preferred going to prison – it was Brixton he went to. He once suggested I went to prison instead of paying my rates, but I didn't like the thought of being shut up and when I made a few enquiries about

Holloway I heard it was perfectly beastly there and not to be compared to Brixton.

Mr Fox used to drive his own car to prison, but first he would call at the police station and be officially arrested. The warrant officer was a friend of his and after his arrest they used to go to a pub called 'The King's Guest' and have some drinks. Once I went with them and it was most interesting. When we had had some drinks and the warrant officer had collected an ordinary policeman to accompany us, we set off to Brixton. On the way we stopped at another pub and Mr Fox gave us all a substantial lunch – the policeman had his in the public bar. When we had finished lunch we felt rather sleepy and a bit drunk, but we managed to reach the gaol and Mr Fox picked up his suitcase and jumped out of the car and gave me a few last-minute instructions about his dog. Then he gave the policeman a tip and walked through the prison gates with a suitcase and the warrant officer who eventually returned without him. The policeman drove us home and everything suddenly seemed rather flat.

I went to see him once during his last visit to the prison. On the way there I lost my way and felt shy of asking people how to get there. After a lot of wandering I arrived at a large place I thought was the prison, but it proved to be the waterworks and they seemed quite surprised when I asked to see No. 779106. But eventually I found the right place and a man with a key opened a little gate inside a large one for me to pass through. He locked the door behind me and kept doing masses of locking and clanking of keys and I felt terrified I'd never escape again. I began to believe they had been wanting to lock me up for a long time and it was all a trick to catch me.

I was put in a clean green room that was very warm, and I sat on a bench and waited there while they went to see if I could see Mr Fox, only they called him a number. They took the parcel of clean shirts I'd brought away. After a time they came back and said I could see Mr Fox, although it wasn't visiting day, and I was taken to a queer passage place divided into compartments and behind a piece of wire gauze there was Mr Fox looking rather jaunty. He wore an ordinary suit of his own, no broad arrows or anything like that. The wire gauze resembled the stuff you sometimes see in old-fashioned bank windows and some tailors have it, too. We talked for a time, but it was most difficult to think of anything to say and that jaunty air was disconcerting. I'd expected to see him all haggard and wan and had dressed myself completely in black. I was very glad when they said it was time to go and it seemed wonderful when I'd passed through all the doors and was free again. Mr Fox didn't feel like that; he rather enjoyed sewing mail bags and the peacefulness of prison life, and it was nice for him to know that every day a pound or so was knocked off his debt to the borough council. He said the only time he ever read books was in prison. Sometimes he would write to me and once he wrote me a letter on toilet paper just like ordinary brown paper, and gave it to a friend who was leaving prison to smuggle to me. The usual prison letters were on better paper with the prisoner's number on top. I think they were allowed to write two a week.

In time he became quite bored with going to prison, so he had to pay his rates and this left him short of money and depressed him. Then he thought it would be a good thing to have a rent collector to collect the rents of his three houses. The rent collector was to be paid thirty shillings a week but had to deposit one hundred pounds with Mr Fox as security before he could be trusted to collect the rents. A little man with a hundred pounds to deposit soon came in answer to an advertisement and Mr Fox went on a motor tour round Cornwall until the hundred pounds was all gone, but when he returned home he didn't like paying thirty shillings every week for a man to collect rents he was perfectly capable of collecting himself.

Eventually he sold the leases of the houses to a woman with a black mackintosh shopping-bag. She grumbled a lot when she discovered they were always falling to pieces – nearly every day part of one of Mr Fox's houses collapsed, and she worried and pestered him about this. Eventually he had to grow another beard in a hurry to escape her.

He bought a garage with the money he received from the woman who owned the black mackintosh bag and at first it was a great success, but during the winter it didn't pay so well. The kind of young man who buys second-hand sports cars often can only afford to run a car during the summer. Then there was another blow – the tax on cars was increased and as most of Mr Fox's cars were simply stiff with horse-power, it made it very difficult to dispose of them. He overcame the hardships of the first year by taking a pupil – the pupil had to pay £200, at least, his father did, and it worked very well for the first six months until the pupil was due to draw a salary. Then he became an even worse burden than the rent collector.

The evening I went to see Mr Fox to discuss my future he was playing cards with the unfortunate apprentice, trying with some success to win his salary back. The young man welcomed my appearance as a chance to escape and hurried away. Mr Fox suggested we went for a drive to Hampstead Heath and I thought that would be as good a place as any other to talk, so we got into one of the high-powered cars which was untaxed (but he seldom bothered about things like that and didn't possess the red number-plates most car-dealers seem to use). When we reached the Heath we left the car in a lonely place and took the dog for a walk. The dog was called Tantivy and was a foxhound about four years old. It had been given to Mr Fox when it was a puppy because it had had an accident to its tail and hadn't got one any more. Everyone who saw Tantivy for the first time used to say, 'What a lovely dog! But what has happened to its tail?' We grew to dread hearing this so often. It rather reminded me of when I was a child and used to keep newts: people used to say, 'Oh, newts. What do they turn into?', and I would answer, 'Once a newt, always a newt,' but I couldn't bring myself to answer the silly questions about Tantivy by saying, 'When a dog's tail is off, it's off,' or something similar.

We wandered about the Heath discussing our futures. Neither looked very bright. Mr Fox was quite convinced a war was coming any minute and thought the best thing he could do would be to give up the garage and get a job in an aeroplane factory. Then he suddenly said the best thing I could do would be to return my lease to the freeholders and come and live with him; he would try and get a job out of London so that we would be safe from bombs and living wouldn't be too expensive. I was so surprised at this suggestion that my face became burning hot. Although I'd known Mr Fox a long time – over two years – there had never been any love-making between us and except for occasional drives in one of his cars and maybe lunch once or twice, we had never been intimate except over business matters. For one thing, we led such different lives and he was so unlike my usual rather arty friends. But I liked him and he amused and interested me a lot.

While I was recovering from my amazement, Mr Fox chattered away about this new idea as if it was all settled and quite soon he took me home. I'd left Jenny alone in the house and was a little worried. When the car stopped outside my house he kissed me goodnight in the summer dusk. He seemed kind and comforting and his beard smelt of coal tar soap.

I went to bed as soon as I entered the house and I lay there thinking about Mr Fox's new idea. Then the 'phone rang – it had been cut off for a few days but I could still get incoming calls. It was a girl called Fenis who wanted me to spend the following day with her and a Czech sculptor we knew. She said they would call for me in his car some time in the morning. This sculptor owned a very ancient Citroen; I'd never been in it before and felt it was due to fall to bits at any moment, but agreed to go with them because it would be better than staying at home with the bowler-hatted men serving summonses all the time.

When Fenis had rung off, my mind started going round and round like a mouse in a wheel, and I couldn't go to sleep. I kept remembering my husband – Oliver – and our brief married life together. It had only lasted six months, then he had run away and joined the International Brigade to fight Franco. He preferred that to living with me when I'd become all fat and dreadful to him because I was going to have a baby, so he left me. One day when I returned from shopping I found he had just gone away for ever. He did leave a note among the remains of his breakfast on his tray and it was kind of him to leave £27 10s. od. all in notes. He said in his letter that that was exactly half the money he had left and it should keep me going until the baby came. It had been a shock to find

Oliver had gone like that, but a relief, too. During our last month together he had hardly spoken to me at all and had looked at me with disgust, but most of the time he looked the other way. When he had first known about the baby he had been delighted at the thought of it and had actually written several poems about maternity. That feeling of delight didn't last long because I became so dreadfully sick and then when I recovered from that things were better for a few weeks until my figure became so queer and I became an object of disgust to him, and that made me feel kind of ashamed in case I was an object of disgust to everyone and I tried to walk with my tummy drawn in, but it stayed fat all the same. I didn't miss Oliver much when he had gone and quite soon I found myself dreading the thought that he might return one day, but he didn't return. When he became tired of fighting in Spain – and he soon tired of that – he went to America and that was the last I heard from him. I don't think it's a frightfully good thing to do to marry poets. My mother was very much against it, but she was rather a dreary kind of woman and I didn't want to grow dreary, too, so I left her and married Oliver, who was delightful and sparkling, and it was only afterwards I discovered he was shallow and spoilt and really rather affected, and his poetry was affected, too.

We had lived in an attic flat which Oliver always referred to as his garret. It consisted of just two rooms and a cooker on the landing and there wasn't a bathroom at all and the lavatory had a bicycle in it – I don't know who it belonged to. Once I saw a bug on the wall. I tried to keep the flat clean and distempered the walls in the hope it might keep bugs away and it did seem to, but the flat never looked very good because the furniture was the most frightful junk. I'd painted it to improve it a bit, but Oliver said I had ruined the atmosphere. He used to spend most of the day lying on a crimson Victorian sofa thinking about poetical things, and he said I had a *petit bourgeois* mind when I did things like cleaning. He didn't mind so much when I cooked; but he didn't have to watch me doing that because I had to do it on the landing under the skylight. It was fortunate Oliver had a small private income, because he earned very little being a poet.

Quite soon after Oliver went my mother died and although we hadn't been on speaking terms after my marriage she left me the lease of her house, the furniture and a few hundred pounds. It had made me feel guilty and remorseful that I hadn't made any overtures of friendliness before she died, but I hadn't wanted her to know what a wretched failure my marriage was and how right she had been. But, in spite of the remorse, it had certainly been wonderful to have that money just when things were looking so grim. I hoped Oliver wouldn't hear about it in case it made him come back. But he didn't. Even now, after over three years, I was afraid he would come back and take Jenny away. He couldn't very well do so after leaving us all that time, but perhaps he could if he returned and found I was living with another man. Mr Fox, for instance. That is what worried me so much as I lay in bed, and when I wasn't thinking about that it would be the debt collectors and the possibility of war and ghastly burning gases raining from the sky. But in spite of all these grim thoughts, I eventually went to sleep.

CHAPTER TWO

I awoke to a morning of brilliant sunshine. Jenny was sitting up in her cot, brushing away at a doll's hair; there wasn't much hair left to brush now, it was worn almost away.

We ate our breakfast in the garden which was filled with sun and hollyhocks and sunflowers, which had such large centres it looked as if a swarm of bees had come to rest there. I left Jenny still eating toast and honey in the garden while I hurried about the flat making beds and doing household tasks that had been done by a charwoman until a week or two ago.

Fenis and the Czech sculptor arrived much earlier than I expected and my heart sank when I saw his dreadful little car which looked even worse than I remembered. Fenis was wearing a white linen suit; I'd hardly ever seen her wear anything but a grey tailor-made which she seemed to live in and called 'Night and Day'. It always looked fresh and she gave an impression of expensive elegance, although she spent very little on her appearance. She wore no underclothes except a tiny pair of pantees and never wore a nightdress or pyjamas at night. Once I went to see her off on her holidays to France – she was going for a fortnight. When I met her at Victoria Station I saw she had no luggage and asked her where her trunk was. She said everything she needed was in her handbag which she opened to show the contents. It contained a lipstick, powder and puff, tooth-paste and brush, a comb and one tiny pair of pants. She lived at home with her mother, who was a kind of mystery whom no one ever met; no one knew her address. When Fenis wanted to see her friends she telephoned. Sometimes she didn't get in touch with me for months and other times she would 'phone several times a week. She was always taking violent likes and dislikes to people and thought every Bloomsbury artist or writer she met was a genius. At this moment this Czech sculptor was the reigning genius and her enormous brown eyes would light up like headlamps when she talked about him. His name was Joseph Weis and so far he had had very little success as a sculptor but that was due to the art dealers who, he said, were the arch enemies of true artists.

We all managed to squeeze into the front of the car and I had Jenny on my knee. The seats were uphol-stered in a dusty blue velvet which smelt of cats. Weis was rather proud of the velvet because he'd nailed it on himself. The car took ages to start and kept backfiring and making the most frightful noises and Jenny started to cry. I began to get a bit nervous because I could see two men with bowler hats bearing down on me. Before they reached the house we were off, but the car still went on spitting and backfiring, and there was a sickening smell of oil. When we reached the outskirts of London, the car began to bump about more than usual and Weis said, 'That is good. I hoped we would get to a quiet place before we got a puncture.'

We got out and had to sit on the roadside while he mended the tyre; the inner tube was made almost completely of patches and the actual tyre was just canvas with a very thin layer of rubber in places. It was quite pleasant on the roadside, sitting in the sun, except that people in the villas behind kept twitching their curtains at us in a disapproving way and the lorry drivers who passed shouted rude remarks about the car. Eventually the tyre was repaired and after a lot of false starts we were on our way again. We were making for Weis's country cottage which was near Elstree. He had only rented it quite recently and was very proud of it. Apparently he owned a boat and a lake to float it on and the cottage had a beautiful garden with a sundial, and there was some wonderful clay in the garden which he used to dig up and use for modelling. He begged us not to mention about the clay in case his landlord discovered how valuable it was.

We had one more puncture before we reached the

cottage but we did get there eventually. The cottage turned out to be an almost ruined lodge in a wood. There was hardly any glass in the windows and great cracks had come in the walls and white paint peeled off the woodwork like awful sunburnt skin, and all around dark fir trees pushed. As the car stopped outside this ruin, three grey cats came running out of the house with their tails held up high. They made strange chirping mews, and one had lost an eye. They climbed all over the car and purred round Joseph Weis, and Fenis kept saying, 'How wonderful Joseph is with his cats! He makes them do strange things.' But I felt afraid of them. Behind the cats came Weis's wife, Gertie – I never realized he had a wife before, but Fenis seemed to know her quite well. She was like a battered rag doll with bad teeth, and dry yellow hair hung down her thin back in sad wisps. She gave Weis almost as much welcome as the cats had and she appeared pleased to see us, too, but she couldn't talk English very well. It was arranged that we should stay in the garden while they prepared lunch; they didn't seem to want us to come in the house much.

At the back of the house there was quite a large garden filled with willow-herb and blackberry bushes, and it was rather pleasant sitting there, but I had to get up every few moments to disentangle Jenny from the brambles that grew so profusely, and her frock became all torn. Strange smells of burning candle-fat came from the house and soon Weis appeared with two steaming plates – on them were giant burnt pancakes. He gave Fenis and me one and dashed back to fetch one for Jenny. Fortunately he retired to cook more pancakes so we were able to bury the ones he had already made. They were quite uneatable, even if they hadn't been cooked in candle-fat. We gave Jenny the pancakes to bury and told her it was a great secret because we didn't want to offend the Weises. She enjoyed giving them a funeral until she suddenly realized she was hungry and had missed her dinner. Then she began to cry and say she was starving. Luckily, Gertie appeared suddenly round a corner of the house with a plate of plums and an open tin of sardines and Jenny fell on the sardines as if she was indeed starving, and then devoured quantities of green plums. I dreaded to think what the result of this meal would be. She had become so dirty I asked if I could take her into the house to be washed, but Gertie looked quite shocked and said we would be going to the lake shortly and she could be washed there in great comfort. Then Weis joined us, wearing a bathing costume and a red fisherman's cap rather like a stocking, and he lay beside us on the grass. His wife said, 'Hasn't Joseph a beautiful figure, all women admire him very much,' looking at him with great pride, and Fenis said, 'Yes, Joseph has a perfect body,' and I felt rather embarrassed because I thought he looked simply dreadful, all podgy and hairy, and his shoulders were sloping and he smelt of rabbits.

After we had lain in the sun a little time he

suggested we went to the lake so that we could use the boat. We walked through the woods, which were beautiful but sad and heavy, perhaps because they were doomed: all around men were felling trees in preparation for a building site which would eventually cover the entire woods. The lake was large and still, but there was no sign of a boat. All we could see was a chain tied to a post.

Weis said, 'How tiresome! It must have sunk again; it leaks rather badly.'

He pranced about a lot on the bank and eventually dived into the still lake. He seemed disappointed we wouldn't bathe without our clothes, but it was fortunate we refused because after we had been admiring his swimming for a few minutes a man started to shout at us and told Weis to get out of the water immediately because he was trespassing and the lake was private. So he climbed out and walked home all wet and we trailed behind. When we reached the garden he cheered up and said we must see his sundial, which turned out to be a circle of twelve tall sticks which I had thought were something to do with growing beans. The hours were marked on the ground with pebbles. It wasn't a very good sundial for telling the time. Then he showed us the pit where the clay came from and he seemed worried in case his landlord discovered this valuable commodity and carted it all away. To me it looked exactly the same as any other reddish brown clay and I said, 'I'd no idea what a valuable place Hampstead Heath is until now.' I rather wanted to see his sculpture after I'd seen the pit it had come from, although Gertie didn't seem to want us to go in the house very much. But Weis persuaded her to let us in after we had promised not to mention to any artist or art dealer what we had seen in his studio. Gertie said, 'You see, other artists are jealous of Joseph and we do not want them to know his methods.'

When we entered the house it seemed very dark after the sunlit garden, and there was a lot of cardboard in the windows instead of glass. All down the walls there were great splits and the wallpaper hung down in tatters; in some places the plaster had crumbled away and only bricks remained. The only furniture was packing-cases covered in sacks. On the floor there were some fur rugs and everywhere there was the smell of cats. The cat with one eye popped its head out of an earthenware breadbin, then disappeared under a heap of mouldy bread; the other cats just stayed asleep on a pile of dirty linen. We had to go up the rickety stairs to reach the studio, which was lighter than the room below because there was no cardboard in the windows. All round the room there were enormous heads all knobby and rugged. Most of them had beards and looked as if they had come out of the Bible. There were a few women without beards. They had great empty eye-sockets and twisted faces. Every one was made of solid brown mud, but some had been polished with black shoe-polish. There was something rather impressive about these bark-like people with their overpowering brows and tortured faces, only I didn't stay with them for long because Jenny was suddenly sick on the floor. Everyone looked shocked at this desecration of the master's studio, but I couldn't help feeling relieved that the after-effect of the green plums and sardines was over. I took her into the garden and let her lie in the shade. She said it was seeing all those people made of chocolate that had caused her to be sick. We stayed in the garden and it was some time before the others joined us, and when they did I could tell they had forgotten all about the sick and we were forgiven. Weis made some tea because he said English ladies always liked tea, and although we had to drink it from jam pots, it really tasted of tea and I was grateful for it.

When we had drunk the tea I suggested it was time to go home and at first Weis wouldn't hear of it, but Fenis seemed to want to return too and she persuaded him to prepare the car for the journey back to London. This kept him busy for about an hour: oil lamps had to be hung on the car in case it became dark before we reached our destination, and the tyres had to be overhauled and the leaking water-tank filled, and the petrol tank was allowed a Kia-Ora lemonade bottle of petrol. Then it was discovered the water had completely run away and Weis put several handfuls of oatmeal in the tank and filled it up again. He said the oatmeal sealed the holes. At last we were ready and I asked Gertie if we could wash ourselves, but she didn't seem very keen. She said the only towel was wet because Weis had used it after his bathe. Jenny and I were looking simply disgusting, but Fenis was still as fresh and beautifully made up as she had been in the early morning and her linen suit was spotless.

We got into the car which made its usual fuss about starting and the cats heard it and came running out of the house, making their weird chirping noises, and Gertie started to cough in an awful, hollow kind of way that twisted her all up, but Weis didn't take any notice, so I suppose it was quite usual. We drove away into the dark wood and left Gertie and the cats behind. I hoped we wouldn't get a puncture until we had got quite far away and fortunately my wish came true and we had almost reached London when the car started bumping about more than usual. It was chilly sitting on the roadside because the sun had disappeared and it was almost night. Jenny fell asleep on my lap and that was the only part of me that was warm. Fenis and Weis seemed to be quite happy and shared their last cigarette together, and while they chattered away I began to think about Mr Fox and his suggestion that we should live with him. I knew so little about him really. Perhaps he was an awful vicious kind of man, or maybe he was cruel and bad-tempered or mean; perhaps he hoarded things like string and candle-ends in boxes under his bed, or he might even get drunk and beat people. Then I remembered all my creditors and thought perhaps I'd better risk all these things. Nothing could be worse than all those summonses and bowler-hatted debt collectors.

When I'd reached this conclusion Weis said the puncture was mended and we climbed back into the car and he lit the oil lamps and we drove on to London.

CHAPTER THREE

The next afternoon while Jenny was having her rest I walked down the hill to Mr Fox's garage to tell him we would accept his hospitality unless, of course, he had changed his mind. When I arrived there I found a great fat jolly man standing outside and he winked at me as if we had a guilty secret, although we hadn't. I went upstairs to the office where Mr Fox was eating sausage rolls and drinking tea. He was always having picnics at odd times.

He said, 'Have you come to see the flat? I'll take you there straight away. Have a sausage roll.'

I refused, so he tipped the remains of the rolls on the floor for Tantivy to eat. He just took it for granted that we were coming to live with him and it made it much easier for me not to discuss it much. We walked to the flat which was quite near the garage in Maida Vale. As we left the garage the fat man gave another knowing wink and I asked Mr Fox who he was. He told me he was a bookie and was paying two pounds a week to stand in the garage door to collect bets. He said it was rather an easy way to earn some extra money. I began to feel a bit worried in case my future life was going to be mixed up with crooks and robbers; but if I went to prison for debt, I'd be shut up with even more disgraceful people, even murderers, perhaps.

We went into the tall house and there was a brown dado on the hall wall and a woman opened a door just a little way and looked at us with one eye and I felt even more worried about the future. Mr Fox's flat was in the attics – my men always seemed to live in attics. There were three quite charming rooms with casement windows but only one was furnished; it had a roll-top desk, an unmade divan bed, a deck-chair and a dog basket. It was lucky I had plenty of furniture. Mr Fox said he had engaged a man to distemper all the walls white because he had noticed I had white walls in my house, so he thought I must prefer it to wallpaper. I was glad about the white walls because the wallpaper was so grim and simply stiff with cabbages, or maybe they were roses that had gone wrong. He said I could have new paint and coloured ceilings, if I liked. It seemed a waste to spend much on the flat as we didn't intend to live there for long, but I said I'd like primrose paint and ceilings. There was a telephone in the main room and when I lifted the receiver, I was glad to hear it buzzing and know it wasn't a cut-off one like mine.

I thanked Mr Fox for showing me the flat and went

home because I didn't like leaving Jenny for long. She was awake when I returned and sitting up in her cot picking feathers out of her pillow. I took her out of her cot and let her play on a pile of sand in the garden while I walked round the flat choosing which furniture I would sell and which would be the most suitable to take with me to Mr Fox's flat.

Events that happened the following day proved this to be a waste of time: because two men with glowering eyes and bulging muscles arrived and asked if I was Mrs Caroline Seymore. I didn't like the way they spoke to me; they almost barked. All the same, I admitted that was my name. Then they told me they were bailiffs and wanted to come in and make an inventory of my furniture. I was terrified and told them I certainly wouldn't let them come in – I'd rather be dead than have two awful men like that come and live with me. I slammed the door in their great fat faces. I locked and bolted all the doors and windows and all the time they kept banging and hammering on the door; then I remembered I'd left Jenny out in the garden, so I climbed through a window and collected her. We sat in the bedroom and drew the curtains so that the dreadful bulging men couldn't see us. I had to pretend to Jenny it was a game we were playing. After a time the banging ceased and I crept out and saw they were pressing their faces to the kitchen window and their noses and fat cheeks were squashed into strange shapes against the glass. When they'd finished squashing their faces they started to write in notebooks. I realized they were making an inventory of the furniture through the windows, so I quickly pulled all the curtains; then they started to bang the door again.

It was a miserable day. All the time we had to keep in the house behind the drawn curtains and outside the sun was shining. I couldn't even go out to buy food. The men seemed to have disappeared, but I felt they were most likely hiding about somewhere and knew if I opened the door they would suddenly come bursting in. I wondered what would happen if they did get in. Would I have to provide meals for them? They would take an awful lot of feeding, and where would they sleep? There was only my double bed and Jenny's cot. I'd never like my bed again if those terrible men slept in it. I could imagine them both snoring away, looking like Tweedle Dee and Tweedle Dum. Perhaps it wouldn't matter very much if they did ruin my bed, because they were going to take it away in any case.

Just after tea there was some more knocking on the door and I looked between the curtains and there was Mr Fox. It was such a relief to see his red beard. I opened the door and bolted it again as soon as he came in. He looked around at the drawn curtains and bolted door, then at my scared face.

'So the bailiffs have been,' he said. 'Have they taken an inventory?'

I told him they hadn't been able to get in yet, but I didn't think I could keep them out for ever. We went into the sitting-room where there was still the remains of tea on the table. Mr Fox cut a large slice of cake which he shared with Tantivy and while he ate it he looked thoughtful – a cunning kind of thoughtfulness. Then he said, 'They can't take your beds and they have to leave a table and chair and the implements of your trade. H'm! You haven't got a trade so that won't be much help. Well, I'll be back in about an hour with a van and some men, so choose anything you particularly want to keep,' and then he had gone.

It was such a wonderful feeling not to be alone any more and to know someone was going to help. I almost flew around the flat putting pieces of white paper on all my most valuable possessions. I told Jenny it was a paper chase. Before I'd finished there was Mr Fox knocking the door again and I asked Jenny to let him in, so she took a little stool and ran to open the door. I could hear her talking, but Mr Fox was quite quiet. Then I heard him talking to the moving man, so I went into the hall, but it was empty although the front door was open. I hurriedly slammed it, but there was more knocking and when I looked through the window there was Mr Fox shut out – he had the moving man with him. I let them in and apologized for slamming the door in their faces, but they didn't seem to understand what I meant. Jenny was talking away to herself in the bedroom and Mr Fox said, 'Who is she talking to?' and opened the door. She was talking to the bailiffs, who were quietly making an inventory and my white pieces of paper were all scattered on the carpet. I felt so horrified and sick and suddenly found myself shouting, 'Why don't you take your hats off in the house, you –'

But Mr Fox interrupted me. 'I'll deal with these men,' and he almost pushed me out of the room.

I looked back as he was shutting the door on me and saw both the men had taken off their wretched black hats and were looking quite distressed.

I sat on the kitchen table and cried and Tantivy kept pushing his cold nose against my bare legs, perhaps to comfort me, but I hardly noticed him. After quite a long time Mr Fox came in, followed by the bailiffs.

He said, 'Caroline, this is Mr Liffin and his assistant. They are visiting bailiffs who will call every day and for every visit they make you will be charged seven-and-six – at least, it will be added to your debts. Mr Liffin has been round the flat and made an inventory of all your belongings, with the exception of a few little things which we will remove this evening. As soon as Mr Liffin has gone, we will do this, but you must let him have entrance tomorrow and every time he calls, and you mustn't remove anything that is on his list.'

I just nodded and Mr Liffin said, 'Good-night to you, ma'am,' and departed, hat in hand.

When they had gone, Mr Fox said, 'You had better wash your face and come out and have dinner with me,' and he handed me the list of the few little things

I was allowed to retain. It was a list of all my most valuable possessions. Then he said, 'By the way, you owe me three pounds.'

After that we went and lived with Mr Fox in the house where they didn't like me and there were brown dados in the hall.

CHAPTER FOUR

Mr Fox didn't get drunk or keep string under his bed, but he was very moody and sometimes bad-tempered, usually when he was short of money. Then he used to grumble about my cooking and Jenny chattering and about how much we cost to keep. When he was like this I felt dreadfully sad and homesick and longed to escape from him, but we had nowhere to go. Other times, he would be generous and gay and full of ideas and wonderful schemes to make money. He liked to bring me surprises home – odd junk from antique shops, goldfish from Woolworth's, boxes of chocolates and sometimes rather frightful books and magazines that he thought were suitable for women to read.

I didn't tell my friends that I was living with Mr Fox, but I did 'phone some of them and tell them I'd moved and occasionally they asked me to parties. I felt rather guilty not taking Mr Fox with me, but I felt he wouldn't mix very well with the people I knew.

One evening after Mr Fox had had one of his moods and gone out of the house with his mouth all boxed up, a young artist I knew 'phoned and asked if I'd like to go to a night-club with him. It was a club for coloured people and sounded quite amusing, so I said I'd like to go very much. I changed as quickly as I could because I didn't want Mr Fox to return before I left. Jenny was asleep in her rather bare little room and I felt it was quite safe to leave her, although during the 'bus ride to Regent Street I did start to worry in case the house set on fire and Jenny turned into a cinder while I was enjoying myself in a night-club.

John Lind, the young artist who had 'phoned me, was waiting outside the club, which was fortunate because I wouldn't have been allowed in as I wasn't a member. When he had signed the book we went down some narrow stairs into a very smoky room. There was a small band composed of black men playing extremely well, but they were rather wasted because there was hardly any room to dance. We struggled through the dancers and reached the bar; it wasn't quite so crowded there because most people seemed to have bottles of spirits on their tables, and at the bar you could only get stuff called 'near beer'. It wasn't very good, but John said maybe someone he knew would come to the club and ask us to have some of their whisky. He said it was really only a matter of waiting. We danced a bit while we were waiting, but I'm not a good dancer; I don't know lots of quick little steps and things, so John got rather bored with that and we went and sat at a vacant table.

My eyes were becoming used to the smoke and I looked around the room. There were paintings on the wall, and to my surprise, they were all hunting scenes which hardly seemed suitable. John Lind said he had done them and he knew the horses were all wrong, but he had hardly ever looked at a horse; it wasn't the kind of thing he painted at all. He had got out some designs of beautiful coloured women carrying baskets of fruit on their heads, but the coloured man who owned the club scorned them and said he wanted something really English that lords would like. John said the few lords who had been to the club simply hated his horses and the hounds came in for a lot of abuse, too. He became quite depressed and I was beginning to think I was a dull bore, but fortunately two men he seemed to know very well came and sat at our table and he introduced me and we all started to talk. A bottle of whisky appeared on the table and we suddenly became very cheerful. One of the men was called Martin: he was very handsome in a rather flat-faced cat-like way. The other man was quite middle-aged and small and fair with one withered hand. After we had had some drinks, Martin asked me to dance and he didn't do all the complicated steps John did, so we got on much better. Then John danced with a beautiful black girl who came and sat at our table. She was wearing evening dress, really rather a cheap, shabby one, but she had such a perfect figure only a woman would have noticed the frock. About half the people in the room were coloured and sometimes when they were dancing they would suddenly start to sing and it sounded marvellous. I began to feel happy and excited and thought how wonderful it would be to come to a night-club nearly every evening. Up to now I'd really been rather wasting my life.

Martin and I talked to each other and he told me he was learning to be a barrister and only had a small allowance his mother made him; he was getting rather bored with the idea of being a barrister but his mother said she would stop his allowance if he gave it up. He said he had done something called eating his dinners but I couldn't understand what that had to do with the Law, so smiled as if I knew and said I'd eaten some dinners, too. I told him I'd been married but I didn't tell him about Jenny or Mr Fox. I said I was very hard up and looking for a job, but up to that moment I hadn't thought about a job and as soon as I said it I realized it would be almost impossible because of Jenny.

After a time Martin said he was tired of the club we were in – he called it a lousy hole, although I'd been thinking it rather wonderful; fortunately I hadn't said so. He suggested we went to another and so we said goodbye to the others. I felt rather remorseful leaving John Lind as I was really his guest, but he didn't seem to mind and said he would 'phone me again sometime. It was quite a shock when we got outside to breathe some fresh air, and I suggested we walked to the other club, but Martin said he hated walking and hailed a taxi. He started to kiss me a great deal when we were in the taxi; although he was so handsome I didn't enjoy it very much and felt worried about him making such a mess of my face. It was lucky it was a short taxi ride or I would have been completely ruined – at least, my face would have been.

The club we arrived at looked much grander than the one we had left and in some of the mirrors I saw my fears about my face were quite justified, so I hurried off to the ladies' room. I felt awfully shy there because there were several elegant girls doing their toilet. They were wearing the most wonderful evening gowns and they all seemed to know each other. They stopped talking when I came in and they all looked at me very hard and I felt ashamed of my plain clothes and hands with just ordinary nails; they had wonderful long ones all painted and their eyelashes were enormous too. I'd always thought mine were long, but they were stumpy little things in comparison. I tidied myself under their hostile gaze and stood all huddled over the mirror in the hope they couldn't see me properly, but I could feel them looking. It was a relief to get back to Martin. He said he'd ordered some breakfast and I discovered it was nearly four o'clock. I hoped Mr Fox didn't think I'd run away and left Jenny on his hands; he might even put her in an orphanage and it would take months to get her out again. Then the breakfast came and it was bacon, eggs and mushrooms and some heavenly coffee, and I enjoyed it so much I rather forgot about poor Jenny.

I noticed that the beautiful girls I had seen had returned and were sitting together, drinking coffee. They were unaccompanied by a man. While I was watching them two men in evening dress came in – they were fat and bald and looked as if they were made of pork; perhaps they were rich butchers. But the girls seemed to like them; they smiled over their coffee cups and one with long red hair went and stood by the band and started to sing in a dreamy sort of way. The men went to the girls' table and talked for a time and when they returned to their own table, two of the girls went with them and the men bought them flowers and drinks and the girls seemed awfully happy. I watched all this and forgot to listen to Martin talking about his last visit to Paris, but he didn't seem to notice. When he'd finished about that I asked him about the girls and he seemed surprised I didn't know dance hostesses when I saw them. They fascinated me, those girls, with their elegant air of beauty, although when you really looked at them they weren't quite as beautiful as they appeared at first. I began to wish I could earn my living in such a glamorous way; they must earn an enormous amount of money.

Martin was amused by my interest in the night-club queens and asked me if I'd like to be one, because he knew a man who had just started a new club and he was most likely looking for some girls to act as hostesses. I was delighted with this suggestion. Martin seemed rather surprised and tried to tell me a few of the snags of being a dance hostess, but I brushed them all aside and insisted on going to see this man at once. So we went away in another taxi and I explained that he wasn't to make a mess of my face, so it was quite a peaceful drive and I planned how I could look after Jenny in the daytime and earn huge sums at night, being a night-club queen. I had a kind of idea the very day or rather night I started on my glamorous new life my wardrobe would become filled with furs and evening dresses and below them on a show rail would be rows of expensive slippers with delicate high heels and just as I began to imagine the drawers filled with crêpe-de-chine underclothes, we reached the club which had 'Rose Bower' in neon lighting written outside.

Before we had hardly got into the main hall we met a man in an almost white overcoat and black hat. I thought maybe he was a film star, but he wasn't; he was Martin's friend, Leon Barclay, the owner of the club, on his way home. Martin introduced us and explained why we had come and I felt dreadfully shy because he – the night-club king – tilted my chin in his hand and had a good look at me under the bright light, and I thought how awful it was that he could see what a beastly face I'd got when you had a real look at it, but perhaps his eyesight wasn't good and he was too vain to wear glasses because he said I was sweet and told me to come the next evening and I could start being a dance hostess straight away. Of course, I must wear evening dress. He chatted for a few minutes and pinched my elbow and was gone. When he'd gone I suddenly felt terribly tired and rather frightened of what I'd committed myself to. Martin seemed impressed that I'd landed a job so easily, but worried too; he kept saying I didn't know what I'd let myself in for. I had great difficulty in getting rid of him and he kept moping and mowing about in that rather dreary hall, but eventually I got the commissionaire to get me a taxi and it was so heavenly to relax in its musty depths and be alone.

I had only about two and a half hours in bed before the next day came and I had to get up to get Mr Fox's breakfast. He was still angry with me and wanted to know where I'd been the previous evening. He didn't seem to realize I'd been out most of the night. I told him I'd got a job and he became interested and forgot I was in disgrace. He kept asking questions about how much salary I would get and what my duties were; he didn't know any more about dance hostesses than I did. The only dances he ever went to were Police Balls and they didn't seem to have them there. The policemen who used to take him to prison would send him tickets for their dances and he had a lot of policemen friends who sometimes came in the evening and played cards with him. Sometimes they came late at night, after I'd gone to bed, and as I slept on a divan in the sitting-room I would feel quite embarrassed to wake up and see a bevy of policemen playing poker with Mr Fox. I used to think it was rather a good thing my mother was dead because that was the kind of thing that upset her; quite a lot of things did.

Mr Fox went on asking questions while I cooked bacon and eggs; I wished he wouldn't because I was feeling sick from all the whisky I'd drunk and the breakfast I'd eaten in the middle of the night. Then I remembered that at one time in Norway they used to eat bears' paws for breakfast. After thinking about that I was sick. Mr Fox let me go back to bed then and finished the cooking himself and brought me some tea, which was just what I wanted. He seemed to think the sickness was the result of his bad temper the day before and became very kind and helpful. I discovered later on he always was considerate if you weren't well, when one would really expect him to be impatient.

At about eleven I had quite recovered and Mr Fox went to the garage. Before he left he gave Jenny something to eat and helped her dress, and she sat on the floor by my bed chattering away to herself about this unusual happening which she seemed to have enjoyed greatly. The day went on and I began to wonder what to wear that evening. I only had two evening frocks: one was a slightly dowdy black velvet and the other a very elegant striped arrangement with no back to speak of and a very long skirt which was tight over the hips but became very wide towards the hem; it almost had a train and was a most difficult frock to manage when dancing. I decided it was the most suitable for night-club wear and perhaps I wouldn't have to dance much: just sit at a table and behave in a hostess-like way. I hoped so, anyway, because I wasn't an expert dancer and couldn't rumba or tango.

At nine o'clock that evening I arrived at the Rose Bower feeling terrified. My face was rather stiff with make-up, but I knew I didn't look like a real hostess; also, just as I was leaving home I discovered I had no evening bag, so I'd come with a huge black thing I used every day. I wouldn't have brought one but Leon Barclay had said something about not forgetting to bring my bag. I left my fur cape in the ladies' room and hurried out because some girls were there. They didn't look so happy. One was being dosed with gin by the cloakroom attendant because she said she had a pain, and two other girls were trying to sell a frock to one with a North Country accent. They kept calling her 'dear', but all the same I could tell she didn't want to buy the frock but was afraid to say so. It was a beastly frock and I was scared they would make me buy it if I didn't escape quickly.

As soon as I entered the room where people danced the band started to play, but when they saw it was me they stopped. There was only Leon and a few hostesses in the room. He introduced me to them, but they didn't take much notice of me. One did murmur something that sounded like, 'This is a bloody hole, kid,' but I hoped I hadn't heard aright.

I was feeling quite depressed because the Rose Bower hadn't come up to my expectations: the decorations were simply awful – paper roses climbing up pea-green trellis work, and there were wretched little coloured lights in the ceiling. Leon Barclay told a waiter to bring me a cocktail; I expect he could see I was looking rather scared and sad under my stiff make-up. After the cocktail I began to feel much better and Leon made quite a fuss of me. I'd never met anyone like him before and often I didn't understand what he was talking about, and when I was talking quite seriously he seemed to think it funny and kept laughing and showing me his very good white teeth. He was a very black-and-white man – black hair, eyes and moustache and a white face; perhaps that was why he seemed as if he had just stepped out of a film. He told me about the job. I was disappointed to hear I didn't have a salary, but apparently I would earn much more money than if I did. If a man danced with me he would most likely stuff some pound notes into my bag; and Leon said, 'I see you have brought a portmanteau. You should do well.' And he laughed again and I felt ashamed. He also said I must ask my partners to buy me dolls, flowers and cigarettes, but when they had gone I was to hand them back to the chocolate girl. I asked if they gave me chocolates would it matter if I kept them, and he said perhaps I could if they had spent plenty of money on drinks and things. He also said if I left the club with a man I must make him give the commissionaire at least ten shillings as a kind of tip; and every week the woman in the lavatory had to have ten shillings as well.

I felt rather bewildered and worried about all these things. Then a kind of buzzer went and the band started to play and the girls became bright and talked to each other with great animation; it was as if someone had put a penny in the slot and the wax-works had come to life. Leon seized me and said I was to dance, although no one else was dancing. Round and round we went; it was simply dreadful – I kept getting all entangled in my long skirts and Leon's feet; I couldn't follow his steps at all, and it became even worse when he said, 'For God's sake dance, girl.' There were quite a lot of people in the room now, but none of them danced: they just looked at us whirling round as I stumbled over my flowing skirts. When at last the band stopped playing, Leon led me back to my table. I was feeling frightfully giddy and breath-less, and as soon as I collapsed at the table he turned his back on me in disgust; but as he was walking away a middle-aged man came up to him and asked if he could be introduced to the exhibition dancer, and he meant *me*. Leon brought him to me, his white teeth all showing, and he gave me a pat on the shoulder and said in an undertone, 'Mind you do your stuff.' I hoped the middle-aged man hadn't heard him.

He sat down beside me and seemed almost as shy as me, so I found myself talking quite naturally to him. A waiter came and made him buy a bottle of champagne; then the chocolate girl appeared with a small bunch of orchids on a black velvet tray arrangement, and I had to say how lovely they were although they looked half dead. He wanted to pin them on my frock because, of course, he had to buy them; but I said perhaps it would be better if I didn't wear them because they had to be handed back when you left. Then he started to laugh and we became good friends. He stayed for about an hour and we just sat and talked, and he told me about his business in Manchester and I was so happy we didn't dance. Before he left he insisted on giving me two pounds, and he put it in my great bag just as Leon Barclay said he would. He asked me if I would spend the following evening with him, so I said I would although I wasn't sure if Leon would agree with me taking a night off so soon.

When he'd gone Leon asked me how I'd got on, and I said he had given me some money and flowers but the chocolate girl had just taken them back, and I asked if I could leave the club the following evening and he said it would be all right, and that I'd done quite well for my first evening. Then the band started to play some Hawaiian music and three fat, fair, half-naked girls came tripping into the room. They had wreaths of artificial flowers round their necks and they danced and sang and wriggled their tummies, and that was the cabaret. When that was over I was feeling half asleep, but Leon said I was to wake up and be introduced to some friends of his. So I went and sat at their table where they were drinking whisky. Leon said I never drank whisky, so they had to order a bottle of gin specially for me, which seemed an awful waste because I was feeling I hated all drinks. I had to drink the gin because there was nowhere to pour it away, but I hoped I wasn't going to be sick again. I knew if I had to dance I would be. At first I tried to talk brightly, but later on I became so tired I couldn't keep it up any more and became so quiet no one noticed me when I left the table and escaped. When I reached the street and smelt some air I recovered and decided not to take a taxi and waste any of my two pounds: it would be much better to walk home. There was a moon and everywhere was looking strangely beautiful except when I reached Edgware Road, and that could never be beautiful under any circumstances.

Chapter Five

I was so tired the next morning because I'd hardly been to bed at all, but Mr Fox expected me to get his breakfast, and this time I managed not to think about bears' paws and wasn't sick, but felt most unhappy. Mr Fox was quite impressed I'd earned two pounds, and said if I kept it up it would mean twelve pounds a week free of income tax. I was glad when he left the flat because I could lie down for a little; but Jenny made it difficult because she was bored and wanted to go out, so I had to get up and take her for a walk and do the shopping. Then there was her lunch to prepare and I had to plan a cold dinner for Mr Fox.

I dreaded the thought of meeting my friend from Manchester: it wasn't that I minded him very much, but I was so tired my face ached. I'd arranged to meet him at seven-thirty at Rules and wished I had chosen somewhere completely different because it was a place where I often met my friends and they would wonder who on earth I was with. Also if anyone came and spoke to me I couldn't introduce this man because I didn't even know his name; and then I realized I couldn't remember what he looked like, so I'd never recognize him again. I came through the main entrance of Rules after getting rather entangled in the swing doors. But there he was, looking like a bulldog crossed with a hot-cross bun. He seemed pleased to see me, so my heart warmed to him. We sat on a red plush seat near the door and I looked around and saw no one I knew, and that was a great relief. We had something to drink, and although I'd grown to hate drink it did make me feel better and to my great relief he suggested we went somewhere else for dinner.

We went to a small but rather impressive Italian hotel, but instead of being shown into the main dining-room a waiter took us up upstairs and we were shown into a private room. It was very Edwardian, and I hadn't realized such places still existed, and I was so scared in case the waiter locked the door when he left the room; but he didn't. As soon as we were alone I told this hot-cross-bun man he had made a great mistake and it would be much better if we had dinner downstairs. His face rather crumpled up, but he said he had no evil intentions; all the same, he much preferred to have dinner alone with me, also he had some long-distance calls to make after dinner and he wanted to make them in comfort. There was a 'phone on a small table by an armchair, so I hoped he was telling the truth; if he wasn't I could always run away.

We had a really delicious dinner, and I was glad I hadn't had to run away before eating it, and all the time he talked in a comfortable way about his life in the North and his wife, whom he appeared to find rather a bore. He talked about his business friends, too, and called them all by their initals – 'old A.B.' or 'my friend D.F.'. When the coffee appeared he really did go and sit in the armchair, and he asked me to sit on his knee, which made me feel most embarrassed, but he looked so sad I did sit on his knee eventually and felt like a typist on a comic postcard. He put through several trunk calls to his friends: they were all business ones and were about things like 'Old S.S. is trying to pull the wool over our eyes' or 'I shall close in on F.H. – he's a shady customer.' These conversations went on for a long time and I was glad. When at last they were finished I got off his knee because he became all sentimental; but he wasn't annoyed, only apologetic. Then he opened the door into another room and said he had booked a bedroom as well as a dining-room, and I said it was a pity he had wasted his money. He replied he wasn't worried about that, but he felt the management would be rather disappointed if the bedroom didn't look used; so he took his shoes off and rolled about the bed, making it look creased and untidy. I wanted to laugh because he looked so solemn, but I didn't let him know how funny he looked rolling about because I know men don't like being laughed at unless they are being funny on purpose; dogs are like that, too.

Before we left the hotel the manager gave me a box of sweets and a bouquet of flowers, and he looked so happy I was glad he wouldn't know all the amenities of his hotel hadn't been used. My human hot-cross bun put me in a taxi and pressed three pounds into my hand and said he would 'phone me at the club on his next visit to London. He seemed to like me in spite of the disappointment I must have been.

I continued to work at that wretched Rose Bower club for a week and loathed it. I felt so dreadfully tired and my throat was sore from smoking and drinking so much, and my eyes would hardly stay open. Mr Fox got bored and impatient if I stayed in bed in the mornings and Jenny needed attention, too. Then when the evening came and Jenny was asleep and Mr Fox was letting Tantivy out for his evening walk and all the people who lived in the house who didn't like me were making their preparations for the night, I had to dress in my trailing evening frock and face that beastly club. Some evenings I earned – if you can call it *earning* – nothing at all. The men I danced and talked to gave me nothing, and although I asked for special drinks they took no notice and wouldn't even buy a spray of half-dead orchids for me. Not that I wanted the drink or flowers, but Leon would come and stand by the table and glower at me if I wasn't doing my stuff properly. The other girls were very clever at getting rid of men who didn't intend to spend much money, but the only way I could manage it was to leave them and hide in the ladies' convenience. When we danced with men we were expected to ask them to tell the band to play our favourite tunes, and even the non-paying men couldn't see the harm in that until they spoke to the band, who immediately played a little tune with some catchy words about not doing anything for nothing, and the band-leader would hold out his hand and the least he would take was a ten-shilling note, and he made a face about that.

When I'd been working at the club a few evenings Leon brought me some postcards advertising the Rose Bower, and he said I was to send them to my friends to tell them where I was working, in the hope, I suppose, that they would come and see me there and spend a lot of money. I'd become so ashamed of my connexion with the club I'd no intention of letting people know what I was doing, but Leon gave me his pen and stood waiting for me to write, so eventually I suggested doing it in his office, and when we went in there fortunately he was called away. I hurriedly looked a few famous or titled people up in the telephone book and addressed the postcards to them. When he returned Leon took the postcards, after carefully examining the addresses, which seemed to please him quite a lot, and he said he hoped he'd see my friends very frequently at the club, and I said I knew they'd be always popping in now they knew where I was.

Actually, the only friend who did visit me there was Martin, and he thought it was a ghastly place and strongly advised me to leave. This was advice I longed to follow, but I felt Mr Fox might think I was awfully lazy if I just stayed at home and made no attempt to earn my living. He didn't realize how beastly the club was. Then one morning when I tried to get out of bed the most frightful pains came in my back and it was quite impossible to move. I thought I must have become paralysed and felt quite overcome by the pain and thought of spending the rest of my life in some home for incurables. Mr Fox heard my cries and helped me back to bed and telephoned for a doctor, and while we waited for him to arrive was kind and comforting. The doctor who came was a kind little Irishman, and he laughed when I told him I'd become paralysed. This annoyed me intensely because I was feeling so tragic; and then after laughing he told me I'd got lumbago, of all the comic and undignified things to have happen to one. I felt quite disgraced. Anyway, Mr Fox didn't laugh about me being stricken by such a stupid disease: he nursed me with the greatest care, and even managed to look after Jenny.

I had to stay in bed for several days and it was wonderful to get all the sleep out of me – quite worth having a pain in my back. When I was able to get out of bed I could only hobble about, so there was no question of me returning to the Rose Bower; and when I could walk properly Mr Fox seemed to have forgotten I'd ever been working there because the war everyone had been talking about really seemed to be coming. I remembered the war scare of the previous year and thought perhaps it would be the same this time.

CHAPTER SIX

But it wasn't the same as the scare the previous year. The war came nearer and nearer and there was no escaping it, you could almost see it coming like a great dust-storm. Mr Fox sold his few remaining cars with the exception of a broken-up old Austin Seven which no one would buy, and he closed the garage, which was a good thing because he owed rather a lot of rent and the landlord kept coming and getting angry. All around people were worried because it seemed as if their jobs would be coming to an end; but Mr Fox never troubled about the future very much. All the same, he revived his idea about getting a job out of London. A friend who had a small factory gave him a reference to say he had been working in his factory as an engineer for the last two years and that he was an experienced riveter and several other things. So with this faked reference he got a job in an aircraft factory quite easily. He was engaged as a riveter, but fortunately they never expected him to do any riveting and he had to do something quite different – making jigs I think it was called, but it wasn't anything to do with dancing. The factory was a few miles out of London and he used to drive backwards and forwards in his dreadful little car, and when he came home in the evening he was very tired and grumpy, and to make matters worse he cut off his beard because he thought it unsuitable for factory wear. He looked awful without it, partly because his face was half white and the other part brown, kind of piebald. Jenny cried when she first saw him and kept saying, 'Mr Fox has cut his chin off.'

Everyone was talking about evacuation and all the frightful gases that were going to pour on us from the skies, and diseases were most likely coming too. I wondered what to do with Jenny. I had no friends in the country – you could hardly count Joseph Weis. Then someone gave me the address of a children's home in Hendon that had a branch in the country, so I got in touch with the matron and she said she would take Jenny to her country home for a time while I was making my arrangements to leave London. It was going to cost two pounds ten shillings a week to board Jenny out, and I only had ten pounds left; so I gave it to the matron, and felt it was worth paying ten pounds to know that Jenny was safe for at least a month. I felt pretty dreadful when I left her at Hendon. She didn't like being there at all although I told her she was going for a lovely holiday in the country. Then she said, 'What is the country like?', and I suddenly realized that except for a few drives in cars she had never been out of London, and I felt guilty and sad.

The flat seemed very empty when I returned home. The other people in the house were making a vacant room in the basement into a gas-proof air-raid shelter; they didn't ask me to help so I sat with Tantivy and waited for Mr Fox to return from his jig-making.

Mr Fox told me there were a number of empty houses on a building site near the factory and suggested I came and looked at them. He said there were building sites all around that neighbourhood and it would be quite easy to find something fairly suitable. I liked the thought of house-hunting even if it meant only looking at wretched little villas.

The following afternoon I travelled to Straws – that was the name of the town where Mr Fox's factory was. I had to travel in the guard's van because I had Tantivy with me, and he kept sniffing at the pigeons which were strewn about the van in wicker baskets. I dragged him to a small window and we looked out at the factories that lined the railway all the way to Straws. It took us about half an hour to get there and when we climbed out of the van on to the station, we almost returned again. Straws Station was the kind of dreary place you pass in a train and think, 'Thank God I don't live there!' It gave me a kind of homesick feeling. When I came out of the station there was the town, and it was such a miserable place. To my right, there was a street of mean little shops filled with cheap rubbish, and on my left the factories; but there were trees in the distance and quite a lot of green, so I went the factory way.

After I had passed the factories there were the building estates. Most of the houses were already finished, but all around were piles of builders' materials. The first group of houses I came to were called 'Pluto Pleasure Homes', but they were for sale on the instalment plan so I passed on. Then I saw a large board with 'Henry VIII Hygienic Homes' written on it, and there was one house with 'Office' painted on the door, so I went in and asked to be shown a hygienic home. A man showed me over the house, which cost only twenty-five shillings a week. The bathroom was lovely but the rest of the rooms were pokey and had the most frightful futuristic wallpapers except for the drawing-room, which they called 'the lounge', and that had orange-and-blue galleons all over the walls – very large galleons. I asked if I could distemper over the present papers, and the man was so shocked he almost turned me out of the house. He said they had thousands of houses all over the country and they were all papered in exactly the same way and were always very much admired, and he suggested I should try for a council house – it would suit me much better. So I left King Henry's Homes under a cloud.

I wandered on to the outskirts of Straws and came

to a wooden archway with 'Happy Orchard Homes' written on it, and there were some tiny houses built in what must have been a real orchard until quite recently. There were only about twenty-five houses built so far, and they were all on the same side of the road and had a view of a field and orchard in front, and there were woods behind. In a corner of the orchard there was a deserted Victorian farmhouse and some decayed buildings which must have been a kind of market garden once before Happy Homes came along. I walked down the rough concrete road and discovered a small hut called 'Office', and inside was rather a handsome man, dark and romantic, a little like Gary Cooper. I asked him if he had any houses to let and he said there would be one in a fortnight and the rent was twenty-two shillings and sixpence a week. He showed me over an empty house that someone was moving into the following day and said as all the houses were exactly the same it didn't matter which one I saw. It was a really dreadful little house and seemed as if it was made of asbestos and cardboard. There were only four rooms, scullery and bathroom – with white tiles on the walls, but they only came half way up. A boiler in the dining-room heated the water. At the back of the house there was a garden, but it was only a mess of heavy brown clay strewn with rubbish; but I hoped that perhaps the garden of our house might be better – there could even be an apple tree left over from the orchard. Most of the walls in the rooms were distempered but very dirty, but the builder promised he would re-distemper our house any colour I liked, so I said I'd prefer white. Then I tried to ask a few business-like questions so that Mr Fox would think I'd been efficient. I asked how much electricity cost a unit in that district, and he said it was only about one halfpenny and there were shilling-in-the-slot meters for both gas and electricity. When I had asked a few more questions I gave him a week's rent as a deposit. I left him and walked back to the town in search of tea; there was still an hour before Mr Fox became free from his jig-making.

I found a miserable café with glass-topped tables and a lot of flies. I had a cup of strong sweet tea and some queer things called 'cheese-cakes', but it wasn't cheese in them but long strings of stuff that didn't taste nice, so I gave them to Tantivy and he became so excited over them he broke a plate and I had to pay for it.

I waited outside Mr Fox's factory and there were heaps of policemen waiting outside, too – perhaps to stop spies getting in and stealing secret plans. I was rather scared of policemen at that time in case they were planning to take me to prison because I hadn't paid my rates, so I thought it better to hide behind some trees. Then suddenly all the workers came swirling out, and it was fortunate I was in hiding or I would have been carried away with them. They made me rather afraid. Their clothes were dark and their faces grey and dirty, and most of the men seemed so ill and knobby and small. The girls looked better because most of them were young and some had painted their faces. There were lots of street traders with barrows on the side of the road; they had suddenly appeared from nowhere. I was surprised to see how the men clustered round the sweet barrows – more men than women, and they ate the sweets in the street as if they were starving. Then there was a great ringing of bells and an army of people on bicycles appeared from a side entrance. There were so many people about, but all their clothes were dreary and dark and their faces tired and dirty. No one looked happy – just tired and dirty, and I thought civilization wasn't a very good thing if it made people look like that. Then Mr Fox appeared and he looked so different from the other men. I'd been feeling alarmed in case he came out looking all small and grey, with a cloth cap stuck on the middle of his head; but except for looking tired he was quite wholesome and like his usual self. I came out from behind the trees and Tantivy ran to meet him and became all entangled in the bicycles and caused considerable confusion.

When Mr Fox had collected his wretched old car we went to another slummy café and had another filthy tea with condensed milk in it, and Mr Fox had ham sandwiches and ice cream: he liked eating things like that at odd times. Then we drove home and found all the people who lived in the house still making their gas-proof air-raid shelter in the basement. They didn't ask us to help, but I did not care because we had got some perfectly good gas-masks and some bromide made into pills for Tantivy.

CHAPTER SEVEN

Y ou could see them, all the children being herded through the streets with their little bundles and gas-masks bumping on their backs. It made me feel sad. The newspapers were full of war, and an awful lion was always appearing on the *Daily Mirror*. The war was coming nearer all the time. Strangers you had never seen would talk to you about it in the streets and crowds of people used to stand outside wireless shops listening to the news.

Now Jenny was away the days seemed very long. I'd rather lost touch with my friends since I had been living with Mr Fox, and when I had cleaned the flat and done the shopping there was nothing to do until he returned in the evening. I couldn't sit in the garden because the other women would come out and talk about me. Then men from the Borough Council found out where I lived, and they kept coming to the house and ringing the bell, and when I didn't answer the middle-aged woman on the hall floor used to let them in and tell them I was upstairs; so I had to lock myself in the lavatory. I kept a book there specially and some knitting, too. But after spending several mornings there I thought it would be better if I went to Hampstead Heath or Hyde Park every day. I used to take Tantivy with me and fortunately the weather was quite good and the Heath was beautiful and almost deserted except for people digging away to get sand for sandbags; they were making great holes and hills and valleys everywhere.

Now Mr Fox was working it had made him become awfully poor and he had to work on Sunday to earn a little extra money. He had to leave the house fright-fully early every morning and returned very late. On Sunday I could stay at home because the men from the Council took a holiday; so the Sunday following my visit to Straws I was washing and ironing all the curtains so that they would be fresh for the new house. I listened to the wireless as I ironed, but I was thinking of other things and was not listening very carefully; then suddenly I heard Mr Chamberlain telling everyone the war had come, it was really here although outside the sun was shining. It didn't seem suitable to iron now the war had really come, so I disconnected the iron and stood by the window biting my nails and wondering what to do next. Then the telephone rang and it was Fenis: she was half-laugh-ing and half-frightened. I told her I was going away, but she said if she had got to die she would rather die in London although she had heard the most dreadful things were going to happen and our gas-masks wouldn't be any good at all. Burning gases would come down from the sky and eat the roofs and ceilings off and eat right through the house and our gas-masks and us: we would be burnt and eaten away alive and everything in England would be burnt up. She said she had had dinner with a very important man and that was what he told her.

While she was still telling me all the frightful things the important man had said, I heard a wailing sound and it came louder and louder until the room seemed filled with it and I knew it was an air-raid siren, and all the things that Fenis said were coming true. I shouted down the 'phone, 'They are coming! They are coming!' But she couldn't have heard the wailing noise because she didn't understand what I was saying; so I just banged the receiver down and ran to the top of the stairs. All the people were shouting and heading for the basement; some of the women were screaming and crying and it sounded awful. I called Tantivy and walked downstairs rather uncertainly because I wasn't sure if it was worse to be burnt alive or face the screaming women. When they saw us creeping downstairs they started yelling that I was to turn Tantivy into the street because he would go mad and kill them as soon as the bombing started. I told them I didn't want to go in their beastly old gas-proof room: it most likely wasn't gas-proof after all. I said I preferred to sit at the bottom of the stairs with the dog. But they started shouting at me and I couldn't hear properly what they were saying, and all around were their ugly, angry faces. Even the men said Tantivy would eat his way through the walls and kill everyone.

Outside some men had started blowing whistles all over the place, and this made the people in the house madder than ever; and a thin man who wasn't married and I'd always thought rather nice, seized Tantivy and threw him down the front-door steps; so I kicked him hard on his shins, and this made them all even more fierce; so they pushed me down the steps, too. There was Tantivy sitting with his ears back looking perplexed and men were strewn about in tin hats, all blowing away and shouting, 'Take cover!' I couldn't take cover so I started to run, and as I ran I heard aeroplanes; the sky seemed to be full of them, but I dared not look and the wailing sirens were still going. 'Take cover! Take cover!' they shouted and I ran so fast my shoes fell off; but I couldn't stop and the pavements were scorching my bare feet. A woman was opening some garage doors and people seemed to think it was a safe place because they were going in, but they wouldn't let me because of Tantivy, and I had to go on running even faster on my burning feet, and I thought I could hear machine-guns, or perhaps it was aeroplanes backfiring. Then I saw I was near our landlord's house. He was a beastly old man who had shaky hands and smelt of drink and mushrooms, but surely he would let me in. A great stitch had come in my side and my heart was bumping and making a banging noise inside me, but I managed to keep on running until I reached the house and almost collided with a man who came bursting out of the basement frantically waving a gas-mask and shouting, 'My wife's gas-mask doesn't fit!' He went to one of the wardens, who was blowing away on his whistle; but he couldn't do anything to help, so he just went on whistling.

I went into the basement hall and leant against the wall, getting my breath back, and Tantivy lay on the floor panting. A lot more sirens were going but making a different tune, not a wailing one this time, and a warden shouted, 'All clear!' so I knew the raid was over and we weren't burnt up after all. The tenants came out of the landlord's flat: they had all gone there because it was in the basement. One woman was carrying a bowl filled with cake mixture, and there was a man with nothing on except a bath towel, so no one seemed surprised to see me without shoes. When the tenants had all trailed upstairs the landlord came creeping into the hall and asked what I wanted. I didn't really want anything now the raid was over, but he stood there looking all yellow and his hair was scurfy. I wanted to escape but couldn't think of anything to say except 'Good morning.' Then I remembered we were leaving our flat in his other house, so I gave him a fortnight's notice, and he just nodded his head and looked yellower than ever and shuffled back to his room in the depth of the house.

On my way home I tried to find my shoes, but they

had gone already; and another misfortune was I couldn't get into the house because I hadn't a key with me and I dared not ring the bell. So I had to spend the day wandering about without any shoes. I passed some of the time filling sandbags in the street; heaps of people were doing it and it seemed the fashionable thing to do.

I didn't return to the house until I saw Mr Fox's car outside and knew he would let me in. I still had poor Tantivy with me, and he was hot and thirsty and I was very tired. Mr Fox was angry with the people in the house for turning us out and had rather a quarrel with the thin man who wasn't married, who eventually said he would leave me alone the next time an air raid came on condition I stayed in our flat and didn't come downstairs with Tantivy.

CHAPTER EIGHT

Very early on a cold September morning a week later we left London in a large open car Mr Fox had borrowed. It was packed high with furniture and it made an extraordinary draught in front and we were nearly blown to pieces. This made Mr Fox rather grumpy, and as most of the furniture was mine I got blamed; also the car broke down twice, so it was all rather grim.

When we reached our shoddy little house it hadn't been distempered after all and was filthy. Mr Fox grumbled as he carried the stuff from the car, and I felt disgraced for choosing such a pigsty. Then he had to leave me alone and face a day at the factory. I felt homesick, cold and depressed. There was a smell of poverty and grease all around. Paper and rubbish was strewn over the floors; crushed cheap powder-boxes, old hairpins and cardboard cartons. I walked about kicking it, feeling sad; then I started stuffing all the rubbish into the boiler and lit it, and in the mud-pie garden I discovered some wood which I pushed into the boiler as well; and suddenly things seemed better: the wood crackled as it burnt and a late bumble-bee came in and buzzed about. I swept the floors, and when the water became hot I scrubbed them and became extremely wet, but felt much happier, and the smell was banished. Then there was a knock at the door and it was a kind, small woman from the next house with a cup of tea; you could tell it was one of her best cups because it had roses on it. While I drank her tea she told me in a sad little voice that she was deaf and her husband was deaf and dumb as well, but she had two small boys who were neither deaf nor dumb, which was a good thing. When she had drifted away with the empty teacup there was another knock at the door and it was a coalman with earrings in his ears. Before he put the coal in the bin he said, 'Are you sure you have enough money to pay for it?' I was rather surprised, but apparently people who lived at Straws were in the habit of ordering coal and when it had been delivered refusing to pay for it. Sometimes he had to shovel it all back into sacks and take it away again.

When the scrubbing was finished I walked into the town to buy food and distemper. The shops were filled with poor-quality junk – five-shilling shoes and skimpy 'art-silk' frocks and ugly mats in crude colours. The food was cheap and bad, too; but there were masses of women buying broken biscuits and slab cake and pulp jam. I had to wait ages to be served.

When I returned I distempered the drawing- and dining-rooms and the house smelt fresh and clean. I had no black-out curtains and couldn't bear to spend our last few pounds on dreary black material, so I bought some black paper, which I thought we could pin up every evening and pull our thin curtains over. Everyone said that once the fighting started the war would be over in a few weeks and people would make bonfires of their blackout curtains.

During the next few days I was frightfully busy making our new home habitable. I painted and distempered and laid lino and stair-carpet (Woolworth's). Mr Fox was too tired in the evening to help much: he wasn't making jigs any more but doing something called 'making a mock'. As the house was so flimsy I made it look like a doll's house: it was the only thing you could do with it. The dining-room was rose-pink and blue, the kitchen primrose and apple-green, the drawing-room off-white, the bedrooms were blue and white and the bathroom pink. All the windows looked out onto fields and woods; the fields were purple with willow-herb, and it was as if there were no factories near when I was looking out of the windows. One evening when it was dark a glowworm walked up the garden path; I hadn't seen one for years and thought it must be a good omen.

The people who lived near us were mostly factory hands. I'd always heard that people who worked in factories earned heaps of money, but everyone in Straws seemed to be awfully poor and their children, if they had more than one, were dreadfully shabby. They said it was because they were paid district rates and not so much as London workers because their rents were sometimes lower; but most of their money went into gas and electric meters. Awful debt collectors were always calling on the people who lived either side of us. The deaf family owed money for milk and to something called a 'clothing club'; and the people on the other side were in arrears over their hire-purchase furniture and a bicycle. Straws wasn't a very private kind of place to live in.

I hoped we wouldn't get any debt-collectors – I'd had enough of them in London. Mr Fox only earned four pounds one and sixpence a week and it was awfully difficult to manage on it. The worst thing was the electric meter, which simply ate shillings – seven a week, just for light and ironing. The landlord had told me electricity would only cost one halfpenny a unit, but I discovered it was sevenpence: he had told a wicked lie. The reason it was so expensive was because he hadn't paid for the electricity to be installed in the house, so whoever lived there had to pay an enormous amount for the current to cover the expense of wiring. Also, if you put shillings in the slot for things, they always make you pay more, which I think is most unfair. We had to spend about six shillings a week on gas, and I used to dream about the hungry meters always devouring our shillings. Often on Friday I couldn't do any cooking until Mr Fox returned. Our food used to cost about thirty shillings a week; then there was coal and milk and laundry and some pocket-money for Mr Fox for cigarettes and things: he'd always been used to spending so much and it irked him considerably to have to manage on such a few shillings. He even had no money for all the odd snacks of food he'd always had between meals – those ham sandwiches and pork-pies and sweet cakes and coffee: he missed them quite a lot.

Jenny came home and she liked our little house and the mud-pie garden. I gave her lessons every morning but wasn't very good at teaching and used to get rather impatient. In the afternoons when the house-work and shopping were finished I used to take her to the woods. They were really beautiful and hardly anyone went there; the time we spent in the woods was the only time I was happy at Straws. Sometimes we would pick blackberries or gather wood. I liked bringing wood home and we would burn it on the drawing-room fire in the evenings and it would blaze and crackle. The women who lived in our road were shocked at me carrying wood home: they didn't like quite a lot of things I did, but were quite kind and polite to me.

Days and weeks passed and the war hadn't ended; it was always 'All quiet on the Western Front'. No real air raids had come and the newspapers were still talking about the Kiel raid; there was a scare that Germany would invade Holland, but fortunately for the Dutch nothing came of it. The Government was always making new laws and regulations and saying petrol was to be called 'Pool' now, and lots of other things were to be pooled as well – margarine and meat and things like that; and food was to be rationed, as it had been for years in Germany, and we were to have things called 'identity cards'. I became more and more depressed and never bothered to carry my gas-mask any more. It wasn't the war that depressed me so much but life at Straws. It was the most dreary, lonely place in the world, and it made Mr Fox unbearable. He became frightfully bad-tempered and nervy and had completely changed from the dashing kind of crook he used to be; leading an honest life didn't suit him at all. Maybe he was tired; he started work before eight in the morning and had to stand most of the day and work by artificial light, but at the time I didn't think about him being tired: I just thought of him as a grumpy monster and bully. Meals were a nightmare: he grumbled at my cooking, and I knew he would grumble even more when rationing started. He would have his main meal in the middle of the day – the men came home at twelve o'clock at Straws – and he would return all bad-tempered and in a frantic hurry and would say, 'Good God! how can you expect a working-man to eat a dinner like this?' and almost throw the ravioli or mushroom omelette or whatever it was across the room. He used to say he wanted roast meat and bread pudding, or stew with dumplings. I did make him a spotted Dick once and he seemed quite pleased with it at the time, but complained afterwards because he couldn't bend down to do his work. Now he had become so grumpy he didn't like Jenny any more: she seemed to get on his nerves, especially on Sundays and at meal-times. He used to say she made a noise when she drank, and if she talked he would shout, 'Shut up!' in a dreadful voice, and her mouth would start to tremble and tears come slowly down her cheeks. Poor little Jenny – and poor Mr Fox, although I didn't think that at the time. I began to hate him.

On Friday evenings he used to take us to the pictures, and when we started out he would be quite cheerful and buy us chocolates, and I'd think perhaps it would be better this time, but it was always awful. I would have preferred to have stayed at home with a book, but he didn't like me reading and used to fidget about and say, 'Haven't you anything better to do?' Sometimes during the pictures Jenny would want to be excused, or start to talk while they played an organ thing that came up from the bowels of the earth, and that would make Mr Fox's bad temper return. The journey home was a nightmare. There was always an enormous queue for a 'bus, and we often had to wait about twenty minutes for one. If Jenny spoke while we waited he would tell her to be quiet; then he would say how easy it would be to go home if we hadn't a child with us. He seemed to think it was Jenny's fault there were no 'buses. Sometimes we would walk all the way home and Jenny would walk so slowly and become tired: it was almost two miles. I had to carry her quite a lot of the way, but she was awfully heavy and I didn't like to ask Mr Fox to do it. Everyone who lived at Straws went to the pictures on Friday evening; they looked forward to it all the week. The unmarried ones could go more often, and the older men used to sing a little song on pay-day –

> When I was single
> My pockets did jingle

or something like that.

We had no money left except the money Mr Fox earned. He sold the car for a few pounds and after that we had to start pawning things; he used to take them to London because they gave a better price there. The only things I had left of any value were some early Victorian earrings, and I was saving those so that I had some money to run away with; but there was nowhere to run to and no one to talk to, either. I became frightened of the other women in the road: they meant to be kind, but I couldn't get away from them. If I hung some clothes on my amateur little clothes-line, they would offer to hang it on their superior lines which went right down their gardens, with props like telegraph-poles. They would say to me, 'Don't you boil your whites, duck?' I noticed the proper thing to do was to put the cinders that came out of the boiler on the garden path. I thought, 'That's fine; I can't go wrong there,' but after a few days of throwing cinders about, a woman came and she gave me a piece of wire netting and told me I was very wasteful throwing away such large and useful cinders, I should sift them through the piece of netting she had given me. I didn't put any more ash on the paths after that; not that it mattered because I didn't like doing it much.

The people who owed money for a bicycle and furniture went away one night; they owed for rent as well. Some of their creditors wrote to us asking if we knew their new address, and they told us about the money they owed, which I think was most indiscreet. Of course, we didn't know where they had moved to, but if we had we wouldn't have let them know. Another family came to live next door – a father and mother and a small boy they always called Teddi. They made a henpen and bought six white pullets only one turned into a cock. Every week Teddy's mother read *The Farmer's Weekly*; she said they were saving up for a small-holding but they had only got ten pounds towards it so far, but I should think they were the only people on the estate who had saved as much as that. Sometimes when I was leaving the house in the afternoon she would catch me and ask if I would come for a walk with her. I didn't like to refuse in case her feelings were hurt, but I knew it meant a dreary walk to Straws with Teddy in his push-chair and Jenny scuffling along the bumpy, smelly road. The climax of the walk would be a visit to Woolworth's, which was filled with women and their children who kept whining, 'Buy me that, Mum.' All the little boys in Straws looked beastly, as if they had eaten too many sticky buns, and they wore hideous clothes and huge and awful cloth caps on the middle of their heads. The girls had their hair cut short with straight hard fringes across their foreheads, and they mostly had tight, hard little faces. The older children were very rough and ragged. They were most destructive and went about in bands and used to swarm up trees and break all the branches and throw stones at cats until they were dead. Once the builder left his wooden hut unlocked, and a band of boys went in and in a few minutes it was just a wrecked pile of wood on the ground. They were always stealing money and toys from smaller children, and often they had scabs on their faces and hands. Every evening there was a kind of roll-call, and you would hear their mothers yelling: 'Ernie! Ernie! If you don't come home I'll give yer a good hidin'.' None of the children went to school because it was closed now a war had come. It was a pity, because the school was a most handsome new one – the only good solid building in Straws.

Winter came and it was cold and very dark. The coalman would let us have hardly any coal because it was scarce and often he wouldn't call for weeks. I used to drag as much wood home as I could but it was very damp and wouldn't burn without coal. Snow came and sometimes we were so desperate with cold we used to burn the chairs and Jenny's wooden toys. I'd always known it would be extra cold in wartime. Outside in the fields there were great planks of wood belonging to the builder, and sometimes when it was dark we would steal one and burn it on the fire with the door open and the end sticking out into the hall; we hadn't got a saw. A plank would last about three evenings. Once we took one when it was snowing, and the snow stopped soon after our dark deed and there was a mark where the plank had come from and footsteps leading to our door. Fortunately Mr Fox noticed it early in the morning and covered up our tracks.

There was a great frost and the builder came and disconnected everyone's boilers because he thought if people didn't use their boilers they wouldn't get burst pipes. But it didn't make any difference, because the pipes burst just the same. It made the house dreadfully cold without a boiler and we couldn't have baths any more. Mr Fox said I shouldn't have let the landlord do things to the boiler, but I had not realized what he was doing until it was too late. I used to think the builder rather handsome and romantic when I first saw him, but he had a waddy voice and would say awful things like, 'Is it cold enough for you?' or 'Is it windy enough for you?' and he called men 'chappies' and children 'kiddies'. Before he was a builder he used to make tombstones. I hated him now because of being such a cheat about the electric light; and after he had ruined the boiler I didn't feel at all remorseful about stealing his wood.

Sunday was the worst day at Straws. Mr Fox liked to stay in bed late and was disturbed if Jenny made a noise singing. All the week I would tell her she was to keep very quiet on Sunday, but nearly always she forgot or would get so nervous and worked up about it she would make more noise than usual. Most of the morning he would spend fussing about his clothes and there was always something missing – a scarf or pawn-ticket or some wretched thing – and he would get into a frightful impatient kind of temper about it, although he usually discovered that whatever he was making such a fuss about had been left in London, or he had given it away years ago. There was an awful opera-hat that was always disappearing, and it caused rather a lot of trouble although he couldn't really wear it at Straws.

There was one nice thing we did on Sunday, it was the highlight of our week. Just before lunch, while the Sunday joint was roasting, we used to walk through an orchard to a charming little pub that must have been built when Straws was only a village. We would have a glass of very good sherry there, and sometimes if we could afford it two glasses, and suddenly for a few minutes Mr Fox would become his old self and I'd feel that any day now I would escape from Straws and a wonderful new life was waiting for me. That was the only nice thing that happened all day – that escape from the dreariness of our lives. As soon as we came in sight of our road we were greeted by the greasy smell of roasting fatty meat: it came from every house. The curtains in each window were so ugly except where the windows had been completely covered in black paint; some people did that because of the blackout. Everywhere there was shoddiness and ugliness, and there was no hope anywhere.

After lunch was a nightmare. Mr Fox would sit by the fire and grumble about the hard chair and the noise Jenny was making in the garden, although often it was other children's noises. Then he would walk upstairs with a heavy oppressive tread and grumbles would come out of the bedroom: the bed was uncomfortable and the room cold. I would hear growling and grumbling as I washed up: it came floating downstairs.

One Sunday, just before Christmas, he was lying upstairs; I hoped asleep. Jenny came running in from the garden, where she had been sliding on a piece of ice. She trotted upstairs to fetch her panda and her feet made rather a lot of noise; then the back door slammed. All was quiet for a moment and I hoped Mr Fox hadn't heard, but suddenly he appeared in the most terrible rage; he was so angry I couldn't hear what he was saying. Then he hit Jenny hard on the head, and she was so shocked she didn't even cry: she just went a queer grey colour and dropped her panda. I took her by the hand and ran out of the house; but when we reached the garden the only way we could escape without returning through the house and past Mr Fox was to climb over the fence, so over we went and I saw several startled neighbours' faces peering at us through their kitchen windows, but was beyond caring what they thought. I put Jenny down and we ran, hand in hand, over the field towards the woods, but when we came nearer they appeared to be filled with boys shouting to each other and banging the trunks of trees with great sticks, so we went to some deserted allotments and wandered round, looking at brussels sprouts that had become frost-bitten and smelt awful. Jenny was strangely quiet, and I became worried in case she had got a complex for life, and I talked to her about a beautiful new home we were going to live in away from Mr Fox.

We grew rather tired of walking and eventually sat on a manure heap; it wasn't the usual warm kind but a frozen one. It was cold there on the manure heap, and we became very sad. We had been out a long time and darkness was coming. Jenny was leaning against me almost asleep and I sat thinking. We must be what people called 'square pegs in round holes'; nothing would go right as long as we lived at Straws. But how could we get away without any money? If we stayed on the manure heap much longer we might die of cold and would most likely have a pauper's funeral. There had already been one in our road, and all the other people who lived there said it was disgraceful; but it had looked to me very much like any other funeral except that there weren't any flowers and it was all rather quick and jerky, like an early Charlie Chaplin film.

It had become quite dark, and I knew for Jenny's sake I must go home and face Mr Fox, so I carried her through the fields towards our beastly little house. When I reached it, Tantivy heard us coming and started to bark excitedly, and I guessed Mr Fox would know we had returned. I dared not knock at the door and felt so scared when I heard his footsteps in the hall I almost wet myself. Then he opened the door and his back was against the light and I couldn't see him properly, but his large ears seemed to be sticking out in a menacing way. To my relief he told me in quite a kind voice to come in; and when he saw how cold we were he made us sit by the fire while he made some tea. He was really awfully kind. Fortunately Jenny didn't notice we were burning her Noah's ark.

Chapter Nine

Christmas came and I made a cake with soldiers on it and a pudding. Mr Fox wasn't so fierce as usual. He even filled Jenny and me a stocking each; mine was full of little surprises all wrapped separately in tissue paper. I gave him a rather awful scarf. Christmas made us get a little behind with the rent and the landlord wrote a rude letter; but I expect most of the people who lived on his estate had rude letters as well because their children appeared on Boxing Day with wonderful toys – giant teddy-bears and cars and tricycles.

As soon as Christmas was over and Mr Fox became fierce again I told him I was going to advertise in the *Daily Telegraph* for a job where I would be allowed to take Jenny. He didn't want me to go at first, but we discussed it in quite a friendly way and he agreed that life at Straws was impossible. So instead of paying the milk bill that week I spent the money on an advertisement saying I wanted a job as cook-housekeeper where I was allowed to have my child with me. I hated the idea of that kind of work and living in someone's house and being bossed about by some frightful woman, but I thought that at least it would be a new start in life and would keep me going until something wonderful happened. In the back of my mind I was always sure that wonderful things were waiting for me, but I'd got to get through a lot of horrors first.

While I was waiting for the advertisement to appear Mr Fox stopped pretending to be a tough workman and became an ill one instead, and it was almost worse. He kept weighing himself and saying he was losing weight although he looked quite fat really; but perhaps he was missing his little snacks and cakes and all the little oddments he used to have between meals. Then one of his eyes went all red and he couldn't go to work and had to visit Moorfields Eye Hospital and wait in a queue there for hours, and this drove him almost mad because he was so impatient, and his eye really must have given him considerable pain. Then he thought he had rheumatism, and for a few days it was cancer in his back. Then toothache came and he discovered a decayed tooth, and when he visited a local dentist it turned out to be a very bad dentist, who broke the tooth as he was pulling it out and left a frightful stump in his mouth, which of course made him even more angry than usual. I felt sorry for him, but hoped we would be able to leave very soon.

People who lived at Straws were always getting skin diseases and boils and ulcers, and one day a dreadful thing came on the end of my finger and the woman next door said it was called a 'whitlow'. It was a wretched thing to have and I hoped Mr Fox wouldn't get one as well or he might shoot us.

One day an envelope simply stuffed with letters came from the *Daily Telegraph* and they were all answers to my advertisement. I'd expected about two. It was quite amusing sorting them out. I threw away all the ones from old invalid ladies because I felt they were too depressing, and there were several letters from schools who offered to take Jenny for nothing if I would cook for the school in return; but I didn't want to live in a girls' school. Quite a number of lonely bachelors wrote, too; but Mr Fox had made me rather tired of bachelors. I read all the letters most carefully and answered the ten I considered the most suitable.

I sold my earrings for five pounds and bought several gingham overalls, and there was still some money left to pay our travelling expenses to wherever we were going. Then I waited for the replies to my letters. A ghastly Australian widower from Watford came in person. He just poked his head through the window one morning; fortunately Mr Fox wasn't there. He wore a huge hat and a teddy-bear coat and I disliked him very much and told him I'd already got a job, and he seemed quite disappointed and said he was sure we would have got on very well together and been 'quite matey'. It took me a long time to get rid of him.

All the women who answered my letters wanted references and of course I hadn't got any, so had to get Mr Fox to write one, which was a nuisance because I didn't want any more help from him and I'd almost made up my mind to keep my new address secret. Eventually I decided to go to a middle-aged widow who lived in Suffolk, quite close to the sea. I was to be a kind of cook-housekeeper-companion all rolled into one. She seemed quite nice from her letters, but a bit fussy, and I hoped I'd be allowed to be alone sometimes and not have to be a companion to her all the time.

One snowy morning in January Mr Fox, wearing a black eyeshade on his bad eye, carried my trunks to the station; there weren't any taxis in Straws. Jenny and I were on our way to Suffolk and Mr Fox came with us as far as Liverpool Street station. Jenny was thrilled with the barrage-balloons, which she had never seen before; but we were quiet and depressed. We ate some sandwiches in the refreshment-room, which seemed to be filled with greenish-grey air, and although I had a glass of whisky things didn't seem any better. Then we went onto the slushy station and Mr Fox put our luggage into a compartment that smelt of gas and smoke; we couldn't have a porter because of buying the whisky. Then we were in the train and had said goodbye to Mr Fox, who stood on the platform with his eye under the black shade and his hat in his hand, and he looked shabby and crushed, almost like the other men I'd seen coming out of his factory. The train started to move and Mr Fox grew smaller and smaller until he had gone and I'd got to face the strange widow I was going to work for and live in a house where nothing belonged to me. I began to worry about my cooking – my pastry, in particular.

The train didn't move very quickly because of the snow on the line. Fortunately we had the carriage to ourselves, and when Jenny had finished reading her comic paper I gave her a pair of scissors to cut it up and it kept her busy until we reached Suffolk. The snow became very deep and we kept stopping. Rather drunk sailors kept passing our carriage window, and when the train stopped you could hear them singing in a dreary, drunken way. Everything seemed very hopeless, but I tried to comfort myself with the thought that at least we had left Straws forever.

At last we reached our destination and stood on the platform waiting for someone to claim us, but no one did. It was getting dark, and after standing on the station looking miserable for about twenty minutes, I went outside to see if there was a taxi or any conveyance I could hire. I discovered a strange car all trimmed with brass rats and guns, and on it there was written, in large shining letters, 'PROFESSOR BAGLEY, RAT AND VERMIN EXTINGUISHER'. I looked inside and there were heaps of guns and poison and things, and amongst them was Professor Bagley – a fat man with long hair and a moustache with long stiff ends. He said he would take us to Mrs Williams – that was the name of the woman who had engaged me – to her bungalow, which was about three miles away. So we got in among the guns and rat poison and drove away between high banks of snow. When we arrived at the bungalow there were no lights showing although it wasn't quite blackout time. The bungalow was built in a field on the outskirts of the village. There were about six other bungalows, all perched on a hill, and they looked as if they would blow away any minute. Professor Bagley dumped our luggage on the doorstep and, to my great relief, refused the money I offered him: it was my last five shillings.

When he drove away I felt dreadfully alone, knocking at a door which no one answered. I had an awful idea that Mrs Williams had changed her mind about having us and had gone away. There was a lot of wireless noise coming from next door and suddenly a woman wearing a pixie-hood poked her head out of a window and asked in a hoarse shout if I wanted Mrs Williams, and when I said I did she yelled something above the wireless that sounded like 'Isn't it dreadful?' and rushed out with a bunch of keys in her hand. It eased my mind to see her unlocking the door I had been knocking at so fruitlessly. She was a tall, haggard woman with a strong Suffolk accent which I found rather difficult to understand; but at last I gathered she was the mother of thirteen children, all alive, and her husband had TB and they were frightfully poor, but Mrs Williams was very good to them although she had only been living in the village since the war came. I tried to ask what had become of Mrs Williams, but it was some time before I gathered she had developed pneumonia and had been taken to a hospital in Ipswich that morning. Then the woman went on to say, as she dashed about drawing the blackout curtains, that Mrs Williams had promised her a cake but she had been too ill to give it to her so could she take it now because her thirteen children would be so disappointed if she arrived home without it; she hadn't liked to take it herself, but now I was here I could give it to her. She showed me the kitchen and the cake-tin, and inside was a large currant cake which I gave her, and she went away and I was glad. When she had gone I lit the small kitchen range and put a kettle on to boil. I discovered quite a lot of food in the larder. The vegetables were arranged in neat rows – all scrubbed and clean, it seemed a pity to eat them. It was an awfully tidy bungalow, very simply furnished with painted furniture; there were no books about and everything was as bare and clean as it could be. I felt anyone who owned so few personal belongings would die rather easily – they would have a small hold on life; but perhaps she had a lot of money in the bank and wouldn't like to leave that.

It was almost a week before I heard from Mrs Williams, and it seemed strange living in her house and eating her food when I hadn't even seen her. The mother of thirteen children kept coming to see how I was getting on and to tell me of her poverty and how generous Mrs Williams had been to her. She said Mrs Williams had promised her some logs and her husband would collect them in his truck. I told her it would be better if she waited until Mrs Williams returned, but she said she hadn't any coal and must have the logs at once – Mrs Williams would be most annoyed if she heard I had asked her to wait. Things like that kept happening all the time. She would take a gallon of oil, or a pot of jam, and I could do nothing about it because she always swore Mrs Williams had promised it to her. It worried me so much. A nurse had written the letter I received from Mrs Williams and she said she was recovering and would like to hear from me, and there was a list of things she wanted sending on to the hospital, also two pounds which I was awfully glad to have.

Except for the worry the mother of thirteen children gave me, I was very happy living alone with Jenny; it was almost like having our own home. Although the bungalow was rather an eyesore, the view from the windows was beautiful and I could see the sea which was about four miles away. The first fine day I borrowed a rather battered push-chair from the mother of thirteen and went exploring. We walked through pine woods and over heath, and the turf was all springy and we passed a windmill and came to the sea. Although there was still snow lying about in drifts, the sun was quite strong. We had a picnic on the beach and there was no one there at all.

It was the first time Jenny had seen the sea and she ran about collecting shells and stones and we made a castle and watched the waves break it down as the tide came in. High on the beach we discovered some dried starfish, which Jenny thought enchanting, and we took them home with the other treasures she had found. We kept to the main roads on our return journey and there was heath on either side and some of the gorse was already in bloom. The telegraph wires hummed and I felt happier than I had been for months.

The next day a great wind came and when I opened the kitchen window it blew to with a bang and the glass fell out with a great clatter, which made the mother of thirteen come to see what had happened; she said she was going to come in any case because she wanted to 'borrow' some sugar and she might as well have some tea at the same time. She seemed most distressed about the window, and she said Mrs Williams would be annoyed if she knew I had broken one of her beautiful new windows. She made it seem as if I had done something awfully serious and I became quite alarmed in case she wrote and told Mrs Williams what I had done. She said glass was very difficult to get in those parts, but if I mentioned her name the village carpenter might put in a new piece. I gave her the sugar and tea most regretfully because it was rationed now, and in return she told me the name and address of the carpenter.

After lunch we went down the hill to the village and

followed the directions she had given us. We had to cross the village green, where everyone seemed to hang their laundry, which was billowing about in the wind. We became all entangled in giant nightgowns and flannel shirts. When we had battled our way through we crossed a little wooden bridge with a hump in the middle and came into another world. The carpenter lived in a tiny one-storey wooden house surrounded by homemade sheds all decorated with broken china. The carpenter's wife came to the door, and she was a little old brown woman with a smiling childish face. She was delighted to have a new admirer of her treasures and she showed me her pond in which lived five large carp, and at the bottom there were some enormous red toads. There were heaps of teapots, too, with green weeds growing out of them. Across the pond there was a bridge made of bits of coloured china and in the middle a house with glass balls on top and china fish looking out of the windows. Round the side of the pond there were queer toys – a stuffed owl rotting away and a Jack-in-the-box with weeds in its mouldy hair and a wax fairy doll all dressed in shells. There were no flower-beds in the garden – just masses of china stuck in cement, and there were more toys and a parrot's skeleton, dolls' eyes and copper jelly moulds and crabs' shells. Jenny would have stayed all day, but I had to go to the post-office to telephone the hospital to know how Mrs Williams was going on; so we passed over the humpy bridge and became entangled with nightshirts again.

The hospital told me Mrs Williams was much worse and her relations had been sent for and would most likely get in touch with me if anything happened. I supposed that 'anything happening' meant Mrs Williams dying, and I felt frightened in case we had to return to Straws again. When I reached the bungalow there was a letter from Mr Fox and I could hardly bear to open it. I needn't have worried; it was quite a nice, friendly letter and it contained the good news that he had got a new job in another aeroplane factory in London. The pay was much better and he was thinking of giving up the house in Straws and was looking for a flat in London so whatever happened I'd never have to live at Straws again.

The next morning, before I was out of bed, there were a number of explosions that shook the house, and I thought the war had come to the village; but I went outside in my dressing-gown and there was nothing to see, and later on the postman told me it was mines on the beach. He gave me a telegram and told me it contained bad news, and when I opened it it was to tell me Mrs Williams was dead. I went and sat by the kitchen range and wondered what to do; the fire was burning up nicely and the kettle was almost boiling but I'd forgotten all about breakfast. It had been so peaceful living in Suffolk and now I would have to move on again. Was I supposed to go at once or wait until I received a letter from her family? I thought perhaps it would be better to wait for a letter; in any case I couldn't go yet because I had nowhere to go and no money.

I was glad I waited because a few days later a letter came from a Mr Williams and he asked me to stay on for a week or two and pack up the furniture, which was going to be stored in London; I was to make an inventory of everything in the bungalow and send it on to him. He also enclosed some money. I thought he seemed a most trusting man, but most likely he was just lazy.

I made the inventory and wrote to another woman who had answered my advertisement and explained what had happened, and asked if she still needed a housekeeper. Then there was nothing else to do but wait and see what would happen. The cold weather returned and I made huge fires because there wasn't much point in saving the coal now Mrs Williams wouldn't need it. I wished there were some books, but there was only a Holy Bible in the house. I used to save the daily newspaper until I was feeling really desperate for something to read, then I'd devour every page, even the City part. I remembered a man I used to know who lived on a Persian oilfield and he told me that when a consignment of books arrived he read them until he knew them by heart and then read them upside down and backwards. I'd always thought he exaggerated but wasn't so sure now.

The woman I had written to was called Laura Hood and she lived in a garden city in the Home Counties. She wrote me a long letter, mostly about her daughter Dawn who was seven years old and a most gifted, sensitive and delicate child; apparently she possessed many educational and constructive toys which Jenny would be allowed to share. There was something about 'food reform' in the letter, too, so I guessed they were most likely vegetarians. I hoped they liked warmth, because I had an idea vegetarians thought it unhealthy to be warm or comfortable and usually lived in a howling draught; but I decided to risk being cold and wrote and said I'd come as soon as I was able to leave the cottage.

A week later a furniture van arrived in the evening just before it became dark. The men packed all the furniture with the exception of our beds and said they would spend the night in the village and call for our beds in the morning. The mother of thirteen helped them pack and she took some lino and curtains which she said had been promised her. I gave her all the food and stores out of the larder because it was a pity to send them to a warehouse. She seemed awfully pleased with the food, but said she needed one more thing and that was a truss. She declared her husband would die if he didn't get a truss soon but it would cost five pounds; Mrs Williams had promised her one but what could she do now – could I possibly lend her five pounds? I explained I had no money at all, but she wouldn't understand and kept saying, 'Surely you wouldn't grudge five pounds to save my husband's life?' Then she wanted me to give her something of Mrs Williams' that she could sell, but of course I refused and at last managed to get rid of her but still had the moving men on my hands; they had finished packing the furniture in the van and were having a picnic sitting on packing-cases round the kitchen range and it seemed as if they would never go. One of them appeared to be a layer-out of dead bodies because he was talking about an old woman he had laid out who had died of gangrene which had started in her big toe. I couldn't bear to hear about it so went and sat on my bed until I heard the back door slam and knew they had gone.

They returned the next morning before it was light, but we were already dressed and had had a breakfast of tea and bread and butter. Just as they were carrying out the beds the mother of thirteen came running out of her house in her nightie; she was still wearing the pixie-hood I'd never seen her without. I thought it was rather kind of her to rush out like that to say goodbye in the cold early morning. She shouted, 'What about the clothes – Mrs Williams' clothes? She always said I could have them if anything happened to her.' I had to tell her they were all packed away in trunks on their way to be stored and they would have to go now; but she wanted the van to be unpacked and made a frightful fuss, and eventually we left her still dancing about in the hoar frost in her nightdress and pixie-hood.

CHAPTER TEN

The moving men took us all the way to London and left us at King's Cross Station. I'd enjoyed the long drive in the van, but it had been a bit noisy and cold and we were both feeling tired and hungry as we waited for our train to the North. Our destination wasn't very far north because it only took an hour in a fast train to get there. I hoped Mrs Hood would have some lunch for us when we arrived. I thought it quite a good omen that when we got out of the train at Crankford we found a taxi had been sent to meet us: it made me feel much more hopeful about everything. I had been really dreading living with strangers and feeling homesick all the time, although I didn't have a home to feel sick for.

My first impression of Crankford was how amazingly clean it was, the streets so wide and straight, everything so tidy; there were even stands for people to put their bicycles in while they shopped. All the factories were in a separate part of the town and they were so clean and well built they looked like luxury cinemas. Then came the workers' houses, built in crescents with lawns and trees in front, followed by slightly larger houses and some very new churches and public halls and folk-dancing clubs, and missions. We passed all that and went up a hill where there were large houses standing in big gardens; on either side of the road grew beautifully kept grass and trees. Mrs Hood lived in one of these large houses which backed on to a golf course. I forgot how cold I was because I was so interested in seeing this strange new town, so well planned and different to Straws.

But soon I was standing on the shining doorstep of our new home and I became filled with the dread of things unknown and could hardly bear it when I heard footsteps in the hall. Then Laura Hood opened the door and she was quite different to what I had expected. She was much older, for one thing – quite fifty, and her hair was grey and frizzy and pushed over her forehead and cheeks in a kind of 1920s way. Her face was stiff with pink-and-white make-up and her eyes were large and brown, and although they squinted a bit were strangely coy. She wore butterfly-wing earrings, and as I looked at her face I knew what people must mean when they talk about 'mutton dressed as lamb'. Her body didn't match her face very well. Although it was so cold she wore an open-necked aertex shirt with brown corduroy slacks and open-toed sandals. We both stared at each other for a moment, then she told the taxi-driver to take our luggage upstairs. The stairs were polished oak without any carpet. When the driver had gone she said she was just going to have her afternoon rest and started to walk away. I felt awfully nervous, but I couldn't let Jenny starve, so I said could we possibly have some lunch? She said, 'Oh, haven't you had it yet?' in a vague, surprised way, and led the way to the kitchen. She said, 'There are some eggs in the larder, and bread and things, but don't eat our butter ration. By the way, your room is at the top of the stairs on the right; I'll show you the rest of the house when I've had my rest.' I could hear rather a whiny child's voice calling, 'Mummy . . . Mummy . . . MUMMY!' and guessed it must be the sensitive, delicate Dawn.

Mrs Hood vanished in the direction of the voice and we were left alone in the clean kitchen. I boiled two eggs and cut some brown bread and margarine, and I looked everywhere for some milk for Jenny, but there didn't appear to be any. We ate our lunch in the kitchen and felt homesick and sad, and when we had washed up we went to find our bedroom. It was a very small room with two little beds and cream walls and the floor was polished oak; so far there hadn't been any carpets or mats in the house. It was really quite a nice little room, but dreadfully cold and there seemed no way of heating it. I made Jenny lie on her bed under the eiderdown while I unpacked and arranged the few treasures I'd brought with me. When I had finished I sat on my bed and wondered what I was supposed to do next: should I go downstairs and get tea ready, or do some dusting or something? I didn't want them to think I was lazy. Suddenly the door burst open and it was Dawn. She was a long, thin child with a high colour and straight dark hair; her eyes were like her mother's, but they didn't squint. She told me in a high, shrill voice her mother wanted me downstairs; then she looked at Jenny with great interest and said, 'You are here to play with me. Would you like to see my toys? You can play with them sometimes, but you mustn't be rough with me because I'm delicate.'

They went downstairs together and Jenny kept looking back at me as I followed behind. Mrs Hood was standing in the hall and seemed in a much better mood than she had been in when we arrived. She started to show me the house. We went first to the drawing-room, which was very large, and there seemed to be miles of polished floors which I hoped I wouldn't be responsible for polishing. There was very little furniture in the room and what there was was tiny, even the sofa and armchairs, even the table had had its legs cut down to make it children's size. There were a number of toys about the room, so it was really a kind of nursery. All the windows were open and there was no fire, and it was dreadfully cold. It was the same all over the house: open windows, bare boards and no fires. It seemed as if it wasn't going to be very comfortable.

When Mrs Hood had shown me over the house we ended in the kitchen and she said, 'Today I will help you get tea, but in future you must do everything yourself. I never do anything in the house except make our beds, but I don't think you will find you have much to do – we have very simple meals.' I started to put some cups and saucers on a tray, but she said that the cups were unnecessary because they never drank tea: they had herb drinks, but only between meals. I sadly returned the cups to the cupboard. We had watercress and grated carrot and bread and peanut butter for 'tea' and the table had American cloth instead of a tablecloth. I expect it was more hygienic. It was so cold I felt like crying.

When it was time for the children to go to bed there was no hot water for their baths although there was a very good Cosy stove in the dining-room which could heat bathwater as well; but Mrs Hood said it was only lit once a week on washing day. She gave me an extra squinting look when she said that, but I had already told her in a letter that I was willing to do the cooking and quite a lot of housework but no washing, so I gave her rather a squinting look in return.

We stood squinting at each other over the gas stove for a few moments while I boiled a kettle to get hot water to wash Jenny with. While I waited I wondered what had become of Mr Hood. There was not a sign of a comfortable chair or pipe or ash-tray in the house, and there wasn't even a photograph of 'my dear husband who passed away'. Mrs Hood disturbed my wonderings by saying, 'You may call me Laura. Crankford is a most democratic place – no social barriers at all.' I found myself squinting again and gave her a half-hearted smile although I was feeling frightful. Then I escaped upstairs to put Jenny to bed in our freezing room.

When the children were put to bed and I'd tidied the nursery-drawing-room, which was now littered with toys, I asked Mrs Hood what I was to prepare for dinner. She looked quite startled and said no one in Crankford had dinner, but she usually had herb tea in the evening. So I went and mixed some 'So-Jo – The Perfect Herb Drink'. It had to be mixed with water, and smelt and tasted quite disgusting. We sat sipping this while we discussed my future duties; there seemed to be rather a lot of them. I was responsible for all the cleaning in the house and the cooking and shopping. All those floors had to be polished at least once a week. My salary – or rather, wages – was three pounds a month and I had a half-day each week. The future seemed a bit dreary.

The next morning I got up very early to get some of the cleaning done before breakfast. At eight o'clock I had to take Dawn and Mrs Hood each a glass of hot water, and Mrs Hood liked the morning paper to read in bed. I soon discovered if I didn't read the headlines as I took it upstairs I never saw a paper at all; sometimes I failed to know really important war news until days after it had been in the paper. There was a wireless, but that stayed in her bedroom, too.

When I had given them their hot water I helped Jenny dress and prepared the breakfast, which consisted of stewed dried fruit and toast and butter; there was cream and dried grated nuts, but we weren't allowed to eat that. I so longed for a cup of tea. Dawn was never allowed milk, but I was determined Jenny should drink as much milk as she needed.

It was rather difficult to know what to do with Jenny while I was working. I hadn't the time to give her a few simple lessons as I used to in the morning and I could make no arrangements about a school until I knew how we were going to get on with Laura Hood. Perhaps I would be unable to do the work properly and get the sack before I had managed to save any money. Dawn wasn't going to school that term because her mother found it excited her too much. For the first few days she enjoyed showing Jenny her toys, but when Jenny wanted to play with them she didn't like it so much and used to complain to her mother. Sometimes children of her own age used to come and play on the climbing frames and swing in the garden. They would come for a few days and often would stay to tea; then, suddenly, Mrs Hood seemed to get jealous of them and say they were too rough for Dawn to play with and made her nerves bad. It was quite unforgivable to be better than Dawn at anything: children who beat her in any game were never asked to the house again. She certainly was a highly-strung child. Often she would pull up plants growing in the garden and bang them against the house, the soil from their roots flying in all directions; and sometimes she would steal things. Jenny's toys would disappear and I would find them pushed behind wardrobes or buried in the garden. I can't think why she did this because she had so many beautiful toys of her own and Jenny had so few.

I gradually became used to my new work. The cold and polishing the floors was the worst part. On Sunday morning I had to get up an hour earlier to polish the drawing-room floor: it took much longer to do because there was such a lot of it. I soon knew the grain in the floor boards almost by heart. I was often awfully hungry because the meals we had were not at all filling even if they were healthy. I used to buy Jenny milk every day and I registered her with a butcher. I didn't dare to eat meat myself, but when I cooked Jenny's Mrs Hood would say it made the whole house smell and I wasn't to use her pots and pans to cook it in. In the middle of lunch Dawn would whisper to her mother very loudly that she didn't like Jenny because she ate meat, and Jenny would start to cry and Mrs Hood would say, 'What a cry baby!', although if Dawn cried she would hold her in her arms and keep saying, 'My darling, my little darling.' It made me feel awfully shy when she did that.

Although it was February and very cold we usually had lunch in a summerhouse in the garden; often we wore gloves and overcoats. There were only about three different kinds of lunches: either eggs, mixed vegetable stew, or a cheese dish. The sweet was either stewed apples with very little sugar, or jelly made from seaweed; I was only allowed to use half a jelly square between four people. Dawn was always served first and given the best of everything, and Jenny was given tiny helpings which, of course, she noticed. She noticed other things, too – that I was so busy I could spare very little time for her although Dawn's mother spent the whole day amusing Dawn or else sewing her beautiful little frocks and underclothes. She seemed to notice and resent that I wasn't the queen of the house and had to do what Dawn's mother told me to do. Within a few weeks she changed from the jolly little roly-poly child she had been. Now she was much thinner and cried very easily and seemed unable to amuse herself as she used.

We had our half-day together, but there was nothing much we could do; we weren't allowed to visit a cinema in case we brought a germ home, and we weren't allowed to shop in Woolworth's for the same reason. Once, on a spring day, we bought a fishing net and caught some tadpoles in a pond, but I was told by Mrs Hood I was never to go near that pond again because it was full of germs and had been condemned as unhygienic. One thing we did enjoy on my half-day was having tea out. We used to have it in a rather dull little tea-shop, but often they had a gas fire burning and we would sit near it and drink cups of tea and eat buttered toast and look at old copies of *Punch*, and we would sit over our tea and make it last as long as possible.

Mr Fox used to write to me fairly often and his

letters were quite kind and friendly and were the only ones I received because I didn't want any of my friends to know where I was living. I hoped they would think I was doing something exciting and brave, not just being a wretched vegetarian cook in a garden city. But in any case I hadn't any real friends – only a lot of acquaintances, and I didn't care much if I never saw any of them again.

Mr Fox came to see me one Sunday and it was a relief to talk to someone human because you could hardly call Mrs Hood *human*: she took no interest in anything except Dawn and it was years since she had read a book or seen a play or film, and I was never allowed to mention war or prison or poverty in front of her. Once I did say I'd seen a funny old drunk man singing in a field and Dawn kept saying, 'What does "drunk" mean, Mummy? Is it something horrid I mustn't know about?', and I was in disgrace for several days.

Mr Fox wasn't at all grumpy when he came, and he brought me some make-up and a large box of chocolates and Jenny a doll's tea-set. He arrived just as we had finished lunch one Sunday and Mrs Hood was quite pleasant to him. I thought she would think men unhygienic, but she was rather arch with him. She said I could have the afternoon and evening off and I ran upstairs to change into one of my better frocks which I never wore now. As I changed I could hear Dawn playing on her miniature piano for Mr Fox's benefit. Jenny was delighted to see Mr Fox again and seemed to have forgotten how fierce he used to be with her at Straws. She could hardly bear to leave her new tea-set behind when we left the house. Mrs Hood told us there were some nice tea-gardens if we walked over the golf course and through some fields.

It was quite warm and we sat on a log in the sun and talked while Jenny hunted for wild flowers. Mr Fox told me he had moved to a new factory in London and the pay was much better and the work more interesting, and he had got jobs there for several of his motor-dealer friends, but they had been sacked for smoking and going to sleep in the lavatory. He asked me if I would like to return to London and live with him again, but I knew it wouldn't work and thought it better to continue my rather miserable existence with Mrs Hood and Dawn for the time being. I still had a feeling something wonderful was going to happen, although it was taking a long time. Perhaps it was just as well to get all the sad part of my life over at one go and have all the good things to look forward to.

We sat talking on the log, and wood lice crawled out to listen and a few early, sleepy bees buzzed past and it almost seemed as if summer had come.

We walked to the tea-gardens Mrs Hood had recommended but found it was rather a horrible place where you had to sit at trestle tables in a shed, so we went away again and found an enormous hotel with a beautiful garden. I'd always thought it was a very grand private house until now. We had tea there and I so enjoyed being waited on by waiters again, and I ate the most unwholesome cakes which I would have hated before we went to live with Laura Hood.

We went back to the house to put Jenny to bed, and to my surprise their tea-things had been washed up and put away. Usually on my half-day it was all left for me so it wasn't really a half-day at all. I suppose she wanted to show Mr Fox how kind she was to me. When Jenny was safely in bed with her tea-set on a chair beside her, I told Mrs Hood I'd see Mr Fox to the station, and she didn't seem to mind. We had really planned to have a drink – it was many months since I'd had one. We walked to the town and then I suddenly realized I had never noticed a pub in Crankford. We looked around a bit, but all we saw was health stores and fruit shops, so we asked a taxi-driver if he knew where we could get a drink. He looked as if we had asked the way to a sinister night-club and gave rather a leer and said he would drive us to one because they didn't have public houses in Crankford. We went in the taxi to a very sordid little place about a mile away; it was simply crowded and there were children sitting on the doorstep eating crisp potatoes out of paper bags. We had our drink and gave the taxi-driver one, too, and he drove us back to the station just in time for Mr Fox's train. Then he had gone and I slowly returned to Laura Hood hoping she wouldn't notice I smelt of whisky. Of course she did, because she came running downstairs as soon as she heard me in the hall. It was only eight o'clock, but she was already in her dressing-gown. We always went to bed at eight because she said once Dawn had gone to bed there was nothing to stay up for, and I was quite glad to go to bed usually because I was so tired after all my polishing.

For a few days after Mr Fox's visit I felt very unsettled and Laura Hood and Dawn got on my nerves dreadfully. Jenny was rather fretful, too. I kept noticing how unjust Mrs Hood was. She said, 'I always like people to work for me who are unfortunate and have no homes: they put up with so much more,' and it was quite true: if I wasn't 'unfortunate' I wouldn't stay with her a day longer. Although I had told her I wouldn't wash their clothes, she took no notice and asked me to wash some of Dawn's while I was washing Jenny's, and very soon she pushed all her own beastly combinations and things on me; then it was the pillow-cases and towels, and Monday turned into a real washing-day. I did everything except the sheets, and when I asked her for some clean ones for our beds she gave me a shocked squint and said, 'Surely you haven't made them dirty already. If you washed yourself properly they wouldn't get dirty.' I was only allowed a bath once a week when the Cosy stove was lit, and Jenny had to use Dawn's old water to save the hot water. It was wretched.

Chapter Eleven

The summer came and we were still at Crankford. The weather was lovely so it was easier to put up with living with Laura Hood. Sometimes in the afternoon Jenny and I would take our tea into a field and eat it in the sun. There was a swimming-pool in the town and we went there on my half-day although at first Mrs Hood said we weren't to go because of germs; but I made such a point of going she eventually gave way, although she was always most disapproving when we returned to the house and made us gargle, and Dawn would run away from Jenny screaming.

Gradually I began to know a few people in Crankford and Jenny made friends with some children and used to get asked to their houses. The first time I went into one of Jenny's friends' houses it was quite a shock: it seemed so warm and cosy and there was a smell of cigarette smoke and armchairs were round an open fire. I stayed for tea and the table was heaped with home-made cakes and there was strong tea to drink. There was a father and mother and some fat, jolly little boys who had never heard of nerves. In London I would have thought the family rather boring, but they seemed quite wonderful to me now, and for some reason seeing them so normal and happy made me want to cry. Laura Hood hated it if I made any friends, and if she knew I was visiting anyone she would say my half-day was to be changed.

I discovered a free library, which was a great joy because there were no adult books in the Hood house: there were a few vegetarian papers with pictures of animals being led to the slaughter-house with crosses marked on their brows, but they weren't very interesting.

I didn't know the Germans were in Belgium and France until several days later; I never had a chance to see the paper now because it had been stopped in case Dawn read anything about the war. She did know there was a war on, because sometimes on Sunday morning she went with her mother to a house where a number of people gathered to will the war to end and to have some good thoughts. But so far they seemed to have done more harm than good.

After the fall of France, Mrs Hood became scared in case there were air raids or an invasion, and an air-raid shelter was put in the hall and she and Dawn slept there. There wasn't a shelter for Jenny and me, but I wouldn't have slept in one in any case: I felt much safer upstairs. She said we could have separate rooms if we liked, to make the house appear full in case evacuees came. She had had some at the beginning of the war, but they had only stayed a week because she wouldn't let them cook bacon. Then the blitz started and at night the sky was all lit up over London and there were dreadful flashes; some were zig-zag, like lightning. I used to watch from my bedroom window every night. Evacuees came pouring into the town wearing dark clothes and carrying battered cases. They kept knocking at the door and demanding shelter, but Mrs Hood said she already had two evacuees and in a way I suppose she did. Air-raid sirens were always going now and sometimes German 'planes flew over the town, and there were dog fights in the sky which were exciting. Quite a lot of bombs fell in the fields and roads around and Mrs Hood became frantic for Dawn's safety. I didn't worry much about bombs because nothing seemed as bad as I'd imagined air raids would be. Sometimes strangers from London would talk to me when I was shopping, and they would tell me dreadful things about babies' heads being blown off.

Mr Fox came down to see me again; he looked very tired because he had been sleeping in underground stations. The house where he lived had been bombed while he was at work and he had nowhere to live now. He had been given some compensation because all the furniture had gone. It was mostly my furniture, so he suggested buying the lease of a house with it because houses were going for almost nothing because of the blitz. He would live in part of the house and let the rest as flats and we could share the profits. It seemed rather a good idea and I told him to go ahead with it. There wouldn't be much profit, because there would be a mortgage to pay off, but it would be better than nothing.

Soon after Mr Fox's visit an English 'plane that had been damaged fell in the town and there was a fire and several houses were completely ruined and ten people killed, and a number who happened to be in the street were badly burnt and injured. It happened at twelve o'clock on a Saturday morning when heaps of people were shopping. All day there was a dreadful smell of burning and the town became covered in smoke; bits of black stuff kept coming through the windows. All this upset Laura Hood dreadfully and made her decide to leave Crankford at once. She went to an agent to see about letting the house furnished and she told me I was to leave as soon as the house was let. We had a frantic time packing her clothes and making trunk calls to remote parts of the country to find a hotel that would put them up, but eventually it was arranged they would go to a vegetarian rest-home in Scotland that sounded pretty safe. To add to the confusion people kept coming to see over the house.

I wrote to Mr Fox to tell him what had happened and he told me to return to London straight away. He had started work on a house and I could live there. He seemed awfully pleased at the thought of me coming, and said we could have a basement flat so it would be fairly safe. I didn't like the thought of living in a basement very much, but it seemed the only thing to do with so little time to find another job. It was just about a year since I had left London.

Laura Hood and Dawn left for Scotland and I never saw them again, and I never discovered if there was a Mr Hood; perhaps he had been frozen. Anyway, I was awfully glad to know I wouldn't have to wash her combinations any more and that I was rid of that wretched little brat, Dawn. I had to stay in the house for a fortnight after they left. There was a lot of packing to do – not mine, but things Mrs Hood didn't want the new tenants to use. I did most of the work in the evening and really enjoyed my last days at Crankford, and Jenny was cheerful and happy again.

We went to say goodbye to the few friends we had made in the town: they were all in a state of great confusion because their houses were crammed with evacuees from London and the East Coast. I think they were quite afraid I was going to ask if we could live with them, too.

I had planned to return to London by train, but the day before we were due to leave Mr Fox arrived in a car he had borrowed and drove us back to London. Just as we arrived in Hendon there was a wailing siren and all the balloons went up into the sky. I felt worried in case I'd done a wicked thing bringing Jenny back to London, but there was only a little gunfire before the All Clear came. On our way to Kensington we passed quite a number of bombed houses and in their gardens the trees had gone a whitish-grey from plaster, and some had curtains twisted among their branches, and on the roof of one house was a broken old piano.

Mr Fox drove us to a tall grey house with a small garden in front: this was going to be our new home. He said there was hardly any furniture and only bare boards on the floor, but in time we would get more furniture; anyway, it was somewhere to live. We went in through the side entrance because our flat was in the basement, but it wasn't a deep one. There was quite a nice hall with a fitted grey carpet. Mr Fox saw how surprised I was and, laughing, said the rest of the flat wasn't up to the standard of the hall. Then he opened the drawing-room door and it was beautiful. All the walls and paintwork were sparkling white and the ceiling a delicate shade of blue. The furniture was mostly Regency; there wasn't very much but it was all perfectly lovely – the kind of things I'd often told Mr Fox I loved, but I never thought he listened much when I talked. There were some rather beastly chromium standard lamps, but I hoped I would soon be able to banish those; otherwise it was the kind of room I had always longed to own. When I had finished exclaiming over the drawing-room, he showed me the bedroom, which was quite small and furnished in modern light-oak furniture; although I didn't really like modern furniture, it was very comfortable and there was a huge puffy eiderdown on the bed, and he had even put make-up in the dressing-table drawer. There was another large room which was painted primrose-yellow and white; it had originally been the kitchen and there was a nice old dresser built into the wall, and it was simply heaped with lovely china. Now it was to be used as a dining-room although there was a small divan in it. Mr Fox said that was for Jenny to sleep on, and during a bad raid her divan could be pushed under the dining-room table so that if the ceiling fell down she wouldn't be hurt. He seemed to have thought of everything. There was a little scullery place leading out of this room and that was to be my kitchen. Although it was small it was awfully convenient and had an electric cooker and heavy copper pans, all very shiny.

Mr Fox followed me from room to room watching my reactions, and if it was reactions he wanted he was certainly repaid for his trouble. Jenny discovered a handsome dolls' house completely furnished, and she seemed to be playing with it in a kind of trance, whispering to herself. Wherever I looked there seemed to be new treasures. I made tea with the new electric kettle, and as I put the cups and saucers on a tray I noticed they had the name of a well-known hotel underneath. The knives had the same name on them, too. The cupboard was full of sugar and rationed foods, and I thought Mr Fox must have been saving his rations for months to have such a store; and there were tins of lovely chocolate biscuits and fruit and tins of Spam almost a yard long, and tongues in glass jars. It was a wonderful cupboard, and so full the doors wouldn't shut properly, and about six tins of golden syrup fell out when I tried to close it.

While we were eating our tea I suddenly remembered Tantivy and looked around, but he wasn't there at all. Then Mr Fox told me he had been killed when the house was bombed. He had been found about a mile away, dead in the road; he had been dreadfully cut from flying glass, poor dog, and must have been so frightened he had run and run until he was dead. I remembered how we had run together that first day of war, and the tea in the hotel cups and chocolate biscuits didn't seem nice any more and my throat seemed to be all closing. Jenny started to howl and opened her mouth wide so that you could see it was full of bread and butter and Mr Fox became cross and impatient. All the happiness had gone from the room, but it never does last very long.

When tea and the first shock of our grief were over Mr Fox showed me the rest of the house. There were three other floors beside the part we were to live in, and each floor was being made into a self-contained flat, and there was a delicious smell of new paint and distemper about; perhaps other people wouldn't think it a nice smell, but I love it. People were moving into the flats in a few days. I rather dreaded having tenants again, but at least they couldn't sing rude songs about me if I was their landlady – or I hoped they wouldn't.

Mr Fox said he was only coming to the house at weekends because it was so far from his factory. He was keeping on a bed-sitting-room he rented near there. Although we didn't say so, we both knew this would suit us much better than living together all the time and getting on each other's nerves like we did at Straws.

It was wonderful being queen in my own home again. I even enjoyed doing things like washing up now there was no Dawn to say, 'Mind you wash the honey spoon properly, Mrs Seymore. Mummy is very particular about that kind of thing.' There was no more 'So-Jo – The Perfect Herb Drink'; no more combinations to wash. I hoped there would be no more chilly rooms, because there were electric plugs in every room and the cellar was simply stiff with coal.

The workmen who were making the flats were rather an odd lot, in fact some of them were deserters, but no one seemed to mind. Mr Fox said we had to have men like that because there were heaps of rules and regulations about building these days. I thought it strange there should be a law to make builders employ deserters: I always used to think they had to be shot, or perhaps that was if they ran away on the battlefield. Afterwards I discovered I had made a mistake and the rules and regulations were all about how much money you were allowed to spend on your house, and you had to have licences and things; but of course Mr Fox didn't bother about that kind of thing. One day a sanitary inspector came and said he could see a lot of new waste pipes sticking out of the house and he would have to report it to the council. I was awfully scared, but Mr Fox gave him five pounds to say nothing about it and the deserters made the pipes look dirty and old; even the holes in the bricks where the pipes came through had to be made to look as if they had been there about twenty years. With all these new laws it was awfully difficult not to be a criminal.

The top flat was ready and it was let to an old woman who had once been a colonel's wife. She was very nervous and fluttery the day she moved in, and sat at the bottom of the stairs watching her furniture going up on moving-men's backs. She kept saying, 'Oh, my poor wardrobe!' or 'Take care of my beautiful mirror.' Then she would call me and say, 'Feel my heart, dear. Oh, how it is beating!' And she would hold my hand and bump it up and down on her chest to show how much her heart was beating. I gave her masses of tea to keep her going. Then an Austrian family moved in. There was a mother and grown-up daughter and little boy, and after they had been in the house a few days an old mother turned up, and she was all wrinkled and could hardly speak a word of English. Mr Fox was cross with them because when they had taken the flat they said it was only for the mother and daughter and now there were four of them all crowded in two rooms and kitchen and bathroom, and they made a lot of noise, which upset the colonel's widow. They slammed their doors and cooked in the middle of the night, and the little boy used to shout and bellow. It didn't worry me much, but the colonel's widow used to come down just when I was in the middle of my housework; she kept complaining about the noise and asking me to speak to them about it, and she would cry and shake and make me feel awful. Then I would go upstairs and ask the Austrians to be a little quieter, but they would only laugh and say she was a silly, spoilt old woman. Still, it was quite a relief they were complaining about each other and not about me. The people who moved into the last empty flat were quite harmless; the husband was a policeman, not the usual kind who wears a helmet, but a special one who had an office at the town hall.

Except for the air raids and the tenants' quarrels, life in Kensington was very peaceful. There was a small paved garden at the back of the house where Jenny used to play; it didn't get much sun, but I planted a few bulbs and hoped they would come up in the spring. Often we went to Kensington Gardens in the afternoon; it was quite far away and we had to go on a No. 49 'bus, but it was worth it when we got there. Sometimes sirens went and there was gunfire, but we were never caught in a bad raid. But often people would say, 'That dear little girl should be in the country,' and I used to pretend I was deaf and say, 'What did you say? I'm afraid I'm a little deaf,' and they would shout, 'Your little girl should be in the country,' and I'd say brightly, 'Yes, the Park is like the country,' and they would go away and leave me alone.

There were quite a lot of raids that autumn, and almost every night Jenny's bed had to be put under the table. Often she didn't wake up at all, and if she did she thought it all rather exciting, like a super-thunderstorm. If there was a bad raid, the tenants used to sit in my basement hall and the old lady used to give little cries every time there was a loud explosion and put her thin old hands over her ears. I didn't mind them sitting in the hall, but they seemed to expect me to sit with them and make them tea and I would have much rather curled up on Jenny's bed under the table and gone to sleep. The policeman was usually doing Home Guard duties at night, and unless Mr Fox was there we were just a hallfull of women, and they used to say, 'If only there was a man here we would feel much safer!' Sometimes the windows would break and the sound of falling glass used to upset them dreadfully. I couldn't bear to put paper and cardboard in the windows and was always having to get the deserters to put in new glass. Fortunately Mr Fox had quite a lot left over from when he first did the house.

Mr Fox was rather restless now the house was finished and he began to fix his eye on an empty one next door. It was rather a wreck of a house and the owners let him have it almost for nothing on condition he put it in good repair. We used to spend most of the weekends planning what we would do with the house. One thing that was rather a bore was that we had tipped all the rubbish from our house over its garden wall; there was a great mound of plaster and glass and old paint tins: now the deserters would have to carry it away somewhere. As a matter of fact the next house down wasn't occupied and all the blinds were drawn, so Mr Fox said they had better put the rubbish at the end of that garden and when the owners returned they would think a small bomb had fallen and would be able to talk to friends about 'their bomb' – 'One actually fell in the garden, my dear.'

All the deserters came back and started work on the empty house. I had to make them tea every afternoon, and they expected to have buns as well. Although they hadn't any ration-books they seemed to have masses of food and often brought pots of jam and butter to sell to Mr Fox, and sometimes whole packing-cases full of tinned food. Perhaps one of their families kept a grocer's shop.

Mr Fox came almost every day to make sure the men were working properly. He was doing night duty at his factory now, and at first I wondered how he could manage with so little sleep, but he told me there were lots of rubber boats and he used to sleep in one most of the night and pay a man ten shillings a week to call him before the inspector came round. He wasn't a very conscientious worker.

CHAPTER TWELVE

The house was finished, and in spite of the air raids it soon became filled with tenants and we were making quite a lot of money. It always worried Mr Fox if he had any money in the bank. He felt he wasn't getting any value out of it, so he bought a car. He had become quite the boastful, impertinent Mr Fox he used to be before the war, and he grew his beard again. He had to stay on at the factory because the government said he was to, although it was really a waste of their money having him there. It was lovely having a car, although we couldn't use it much because of the shortage of petrol; but he managed to exchange some tins of golden syrup for petrol coupons, so we were able to get into the country sometimes. After a few months he sold the car and got quite a large profit, and then, of course, he was always buying and selling cars. People still wanted them in spite of petrol rationing.

Jenny had started to go to a girls' high school which

had a kindergarten class. I used to worry quite a lot in case the school was bombed and she was killed: I felt it wouldn't matter so much if we were killed together. One morning as I was taking her to school we discovered a rather battered puppy lying in the garden of an empty house. The puppy was so weak from hunger it couldn't stand up, but it gave my hand a feeble lick. Its brown-and-white coat was splashed with dried blood and it had several cuts on its chest. Jenny begged me to take it home and make it better; she said, 'Let's call it Scarebones.' So I took Scarebones home, although I had an idea it would die before the day was out and I couldn't bear the sadness. Scarebones was too weak even to lap a little milk, so I gave him Brand's beef essence in a teaspoon and he began to recover although he was still too weak to stand. After the Brand's he went on to raw eggs and milk and then raw beef. All this was heavy on our rations, but Mr Fox put it right when he came for the weekend. He had gone back to day work and was rather cross about it. He had found a doctor who lived in a slum near the factory, and he said he was awfully helpful and was going to give him lots of certificates to say he was ill because that was the only way he could avoid going to the factory too much. Once when he was doing night work the man who was supposed to call him forgot, and when Mr Fox woke up it was the next day and all the day-shift people were working and he couldn't escape, so he had to stay in the factory until the following morning.

After a week Scarebones completely recovered; even the cuts on his chest disappeared. He wasn't a handsome dog and however much he ate remained completely flat, like a kipper. His tail went round and round like a corkscrew and he had a white face with rather common brown eyebrows; but Jenny loved him. He was quite a small dog and we were usually allowed to take him on 'buses. Jenny didn't go to school in the afternoon, so we often went long walks. Sometimes we crossed the Fulham Road and explored the river. There was a kind of beach at the end of the Chelsea Embankment, and when the tide was low swans liked to come there. There were beautiful boats, too; it was like a Whistler etching. I used to sit and look and feel happy while Jenny and Scarebones played on the very muddy beach.

One day the policeman's wife asked me if I knew anyone who would like to buy a large grand piano for ten pounds; apparently an aunt of hers had one she didn't know what to do with. I thought what a wonderful place it would be to put Jenny under during air raids, so I said I'd buy it. I was rather uneasy after I'd agreed to purchase it in case Mr Fox was angry with me for spending ten pounds on such a useless object, so I thought I wouldn't tell him anything about it until it was already in the house. I felt even more uneasy when it arrived: it looked so huge – like a giant harp. The legs seemed to have disappeared. They put it on its side on a queer little trolley called Samson, and three men spent about half an hour trying to get it into the house, and it made me feel shy having this huge thing coming into my house. Quite a crowd collected outside to watch the men heaving it up the steps. It wouldn't go into the basement so they had to put it in the drawing-room, and you couldn't disguise it at all. They brought the legs in separately and some pedals and things, and they screwed them all on and went away and I was left with the piano. It looked awful, so big and black. I tried opening it, but it was like an awful mouth filled with false teeth, only some were missing: the ivory had come off and there was only wood underneath. I knew Mr Fox would be furious.

When he turned up on Saturday I just stayed downstairs, but eventually he went up by himself and soon came thumping down. His ears were sticking out, which was always a bad sign. But this time they weren't working properly because he wasn't angry at all. He asked how much I'd paid for the piano, and when I said it cost ten pounds he said, 'Good! We will advertise it for thirty-five and make twenty-five pounds profit.' He really seemed awfully pleased and I thought it must be irony at first, but when he wrote out an advertisement to an evening newspaper and enclosed a cheque I realized he really thought we had a bargain.

We spent the weekend cleaning the piano: Mr Fox even washed the part under the strings and it came up all yellow and shiny. A little piano-tuner who smelt of beer came to tune it and said it was quite a nice piano, but it was a pity about the missing ivories. Mr Fox said he would soon fix that, and a few days later he turned up with quite a lot. He said he had taken them from the piano in his factory canteen: he didn't seem to think it mattered, but I'm sure it did. He told me to get some glue and stick them on before the advertisement came out. I bought some glue the next day, but before I had time to use it the telephone started ringing and it was people wanting to buy pianos. I hurriedly stuck on all the missing ivories and gave the piano a great dust, and it really looked like the sort of piano you see in other people's houses. I had hardly finished the dusting before there was a ring at the bell and it was a sad-looking man with long hair and a sallow face. He was the kind of man who used to play in cinemas in the silent-film days. He sat down at the piano and did kind of limbering movements with his fingers to show how musical he was; then he attacked the instrument and great chords sounded and other things, too. The newly-stuck ivories came flying off like playing cards, and the sad little man stopped playing and wiped his fingers on the inside of his trouser pockets, then ran them through his hair and gave me a reproachful glance and left the house without saying anything.

I collected the wretched pieces of ivory and hopefully stuck them back except for one that had disappeared. I suddenly noticed Scarebones was chewing something and found he had chewed up the missing one in mistake for a bone. I began to feel rather depressed.

People kept 'phoning and asking questions. How large was the piano and what kind of legs had it got? The legs seemed to be the most important part of the piano: everyone wanted to know about them. I told the first enquirer that it had three fine, fat, round legs, but they just rang off; so I told the next people the legs were beautifully carved and they said they didn't want that kind of instrument, and after a few more calls I realized that for some reason pianos should have *square* legs. No one was interested in the *tone*. Then three men who looked like burglars came and called me 'girlie'. They said they had opened a classy club called 'The Schubert Social' and wanted a piano to make it lively. They just glanced at the piano and said they thought it looked O K and asked if I'd sell them 'those flash lamps'; and it was the awful chromium lamps they wanted, so I said they could have the pair for eight pounds. They gave me a whole roll of one-pound notes and I gave them a receipt; they said some people called 'the boys' would call for the piano in the morning and went away, carrying the lamps.

Mr Fox was delighted when he came next time to find all those one-pound notes waiting for him and said I'd got to go to a sale and buy another piano to sell, and he studied all the sales advertised in newspapers. There was one where they were advertising a piano amongst other things and he said I was to go there. I felt terrified and begged him to let me off doing such a dreadful thing, but he said I was costing him quite a lot of money and it was the least I could do. He often said frightful things like that when he was cross, and it made me feel so humiliated and sad.

A few days later I did as I was told and went to the saleroom, which I discovered after a lot of trouble in a very bombed part of the city. I saw the piano Mr Fox said I'd got to buy and thought the best thing to do would be to sit on it so that no one else could see it properly. Mr Fox said I wasn't to pay more than fourteen pounds for it. It was rather an ugly yellowish piano but small, and people seemed to like small ones best; but the legs were round. Some of the piano seemed to be missing. I didn't know if it was an important part and knew Mr Fox would say it could easily be replaced if I didn't buy it, but on the other hand if I did he would say I'd bought a completely useless lump of wood and wasted fourteen pounds. It was awfully worrying. I watched people bidding: they looked so shabby, but I expect they were quite rich really. Someone bought a tennis racquet and a mincing-machine for eleven shillings and I wondered how those two things had come together. I wasn't sure which was the best way to bid: some people just gave a knowing nod with their heads and others flipped their catalogues, and some didn't seem to do anything, but they bought things just the same. I kept rehearsing to myself how I would bid and suddenly found the auctioneer watching me and I'd nearly bought a mattress and two flannelette blankets. The auctioneer kept making jokes and if people didn't bid enough he would say, 'Look here, there is a watch at the end of this chain,' or 'I'm sure you ladies would like to buy this Plunkett roller'; and when a man bid for a pram everyone laughed as if they were at a music-hall. I think it must have been a very common saleroom and it smelt a lot. Two hours went by and I began to feel so bored and dirty, but there were almost a hundred lots to go before my piano and I daren't leave the building in case they suddenly changed the number or something. The joking auctioneer left and his place was taken by a dreary, slow young man and you could feel everyone being impatient with him. They had been rather in awe of the other one: I expect that was why they laughed at his jokes so much. He went on and on and kept saying 'er' after every word. Most of the people left the saleroom and I was almost alone with him and a few men in dirty white aprons. Then that was the end of the sale and they had never got as far as my lot. I'd wasted all that afternoon there and now I'd get into dreadful trouble with Mr Fox. He would be bound to say I should have arranged things better. I went sadly home on the Circle Line and felt ugly and dirty; all my make-up had come off and I was covered in dirt instead. When I reached the house the police-man's wife whom I'd left in charge of Jenny was angry because I had been away so long and she was waiting to go to the pictures with her husband.

Mr Fox phoned later in the evening and asked how I had got on, and I told him a long, rambling story; but I don't think he believed me and he said surely I had the sense to go to the office and make an offer for the piano. Then I lied and said that is exactly what I did do, but the office was closed. I told him there seemed to be part of the beastly piano missing and explained how it had looked, but he said they always were like that and I was hopeless. And that was the end of our telephone conversation

The next morning I 'phoned the saleroom and said could I buy the piano that hadn't been sold the day before. They were quite pleasant to me and said they would let me know in an hour while they made some enquiries, and they asked how much I would pay, so I said 'Thirteen pounds' hopefully. I really was awfully lucky, because they 'phoned up later and said I could have it.

When Mr Fox came he was still rather grumpy with me, but I didn't mind because when he went upstairs and saw the piano in the drawing-room just waiting to be sold, he really was impressed and started to write an advertisement on the back of an envelope.

CHAPTER THIRTEEN

After that Mr Fox took more and more time off from his factory and we both bought and sold pianos. Quite gone were the days when I was shy of them coming in; now our steps were almost worn away with pianos going up and down. I wasn't at all scared of attending sales any more, and used to bid with a kind of poker face that I had noticed the best people used. Often Jenny and Scarebones came to sales with me, and Jenny sat quite quiet, as did Scarebones except when people trod on him. Mr Fox was much more professional than me. He used to stand outside the saleroom in something called 'The Ring', which was very tough-looking men who stood in a circle and muttered, and they did a thing they called 'The Knockout'. He made quite a lot of extra money out of that. If they didn't let him join the Ring he used to bid against them for things he didn't want, and when he had run up the bidding very high he just got out in time. The places I usually went to to buy things were much better than the first one I had visited, and although they smelt a bit fusty they didn't have all that dreadful bedding.

Selling pianos was a strain because one had to tell rather a lot of lies. I didn't mind doing it down the 'phone but felt miserable doing it with people who were looking so trusting, and I tried to avoid it as much as possible. There was one lie that I nearly always had to say. I had to make up a story to explain how I had a piano for sale when I couldn't even play. For several reasons I couldn't say I'd bought it to sell again, so I usually said it had been left me by my dear old mother-in-law. Then they always wanted to know how old it was, and although some of them weren't bad pianos they were all between fifty and seventy years old. Often they had that they were made by the makers of Queen Victoria's piano written on them and we had to scratch it out. Mr Fox said I was to say the pianos were made about the time of the last war and if I liked I could mutter under my breath, 'last war but one' and that would mean the Boer War and be true. If ever anyone 'phoned and asked to know the number, he said I was to tell them it was sold, because only dealers asked questions like that.

We had one setback. It was very difficult advertising in those days because of the shortage of paper and lots of newspapers wouldn't take advertisements for pianos at all, so we kept putting the original advertisement we had had in an evening paper. We were careful not to say the make of piano, so that it would do for anything we happened to have at the time. Sometimes we sold several from the same advertisement. Then the paper wrote and said, 'We think it time your advertisement ceased. If you haven't sold your piano by now you never will.' I expect they guessed it was really rather a racket.

We had a rest from pianos and it was quite a relief to me, because often once they had been sold people complained that the pianos were larger than we had said and wouldn't go into their houses; and it wasn't surprising because most of them went to little villas on the outskirts of London. Mr Fox was always careful not to say the exact size: he just said they were about six or seven feet, and our drawing-room was so large they looked much smaller there than they really were. People complained about other things, too: moths and woodworms and something pretty dreadful called 'a cracked belly'. All these things worried me a lot at the time, but they needn't have because although we made a huge profit we still sold the pianos much cheaper than they were selling them in shops, and the price of pianos went up more and more as the war went on, so people who had bought them from us had quite a bargain in the long run.

While there was a peaceful lull due to the difficulty in advertising, we resumed our afternoon walks and often went to our muddy beach on the Embankment. Scarebones was rather a pest there because he would keep disturbing the swans, and sometimes they would turn on him and I'd have to rescue him although I was really rather scared of them when they were doing all that flapping and hissing. One afternoon when Scarebones had been stirring up the swans more than usual I tied him to a bench and sat watching Jenny trying to tug about a huge anchor she had found in the mud. I was feeling rather dreamy and hardly noticed a dapper little man come and sit beside me until he took off his Foreign Office black hat with an exaggerated sweep and said, 'Good afternoon, Caroline.' I was quite startled because he looked like the villain in a Victorian play; then I realized it was Joseph Weis. He was all dressed in black with rather a lot of fluff on it and his shirt seemed to have more stripes on it than shirts usually do, and his bow-tie had stripes as well.

When we had recovered from the surprise of meeting each other after all those years, we had a lot to talk about. He hadn't seen Fenis since the outbreak of war, he said, and he had some official job that he seemed very proud of; but I couldn't quite make out what the job was. He put his finger against his nose and said, 'hush-hush', which I thought was a waddy thing to do. I asked after his wife and he put on a sad, deep voice and said she was dead and drew attention to his black clothes and said he was surprised I wasn't wearing black as well. I said I'd no one to mourn for, but he answered, still in his grave voice, that we should mourn for anyone who had passed away even if we hadn't liked them very much while they were alive. I couldn't understand what he was talking about until he said something that was such a shock I became all numb for a few moments. He said Oliver was dead. He had been killed in one of the first raids on London. He admitted he had only heard this through someone else who had told him that Oliver had returned to England to join the Army; apparently he had been living in America. Poor Oliver, he was always getting mixed up in wars. He hadn't got as far as joining the Army before he was killed in the street as he was leaving a Soho restaurant. It did sound the kind of way Oliver might have died, but I could hardly believe it. My one idea was to escape Joseph Weis, which was difficult, and I had to give him my address before I was allowed to go. I collected a very muddy Jenny and hurried a little way along the Embankment; then I heard Scarebones yelping and I'd still left him tied to the bench, so I had to return and say more goodbyes to Joseph and escape all over again.

When I reached home I could think of nothing except that Oliver was dead. I found I was almost pretending to myself that I was sad, but in my heart I wasn't. Oliver was such a shadowy person to me I could hardly remember how he looked. Then I realized that in future when I filled in forms I would have to put 'Widow' and wondered if I was eligible for a widow's pension, but thought I'd rather do without one unless I were starving.

It took me several days before I could bring myself to make any enquiries, and when I did I pretended I was just a friend. I was given the date of Oliver's death and it had happened just as Joseph Weis had said; so I was undoubtedly a widow. I decided I wouldn't tell Mr Fox in case he thought we should get married; it was much better as it was.

Then I almost forgot all about Oliver again because Mr Fox suddenly said we were going to move so that we would have a new address to sell pianos from and more room. I didn't really mind about moving because the perpetual battle between the colonel's widow and the Austrians was getting on my nerves, and the policeman's wife was always cooking fish in the middle of the afternoon and it smelt awful.

Although houses were getting scarce we found one quite easily: it was rather bombed but very charming and small, almost a cottage. It was in a little turning on the Kensington side of the Fulham Road. It had a nice garden with a little shed in it. In one of the upstairs rooms we found a great hole in the ceiling that rain came through. But the most interesting thing about it was that in a corner there was a whole stack of furniture and useful things like baskets for dirty clothes. There were four quite nice Victorian chairs with wicker seats, and some cupboards, and a little bedside table and a large and ugly clock that chimed. I knew I could make that clock lovely if I painted it white and put cupids and flowers on it. The cupboards were a bit ugly, too, but I could pickle them, perhaps.

Mr Fox always became very excited when he was

working on a house and bossing the deserters about. He used to shout and bully them all day, but they didn't really mind because he paid them well and gave them masses of tea and sticky buns. If I was there I had to make the tea. I polished up the chairs and stripped some of the furniture and painted the rest pale blue. There was a delightful half-circular table with a loose leg which one of the deserters mended for me. Then one day the agent who had let us the house said the previous owner had been in touch with them about some furniture he had left in one of the bedrooms and he would be sending a van to collect it in a few days. I was horrified. There was the clock all painted white with one cupid on it already; and the bedside cupboards were ghosts of their former selves now they were stripped, and there was an old-fashioned washstand I'd had the back cut off, and lots of the furniture was blue now.

Mr Fox wasn't there when the agent came and I managed to get rid of him without showing how upset I was, but I was so frightened I would have gladly died. I thought I would most likely be sent to prison for damaging other people's property. I wondered if Mr Fox would bail me out. I felt too frightened to work in the house any more, and went home and smelt the policeman's fish cooking. All that night I couldn't sleep, but just as the light was beginning to come I thought of an idea. I would write a letter and say what I had done and say how sorry I was. I knew Mr Fox would not agree with this because it would be admitting my guilt and they might make me pay a lot of money for compensation, but that would be better than going to prison.

As soon as I'd taken Jenny to school I sat down to write my letter. I ate quite half my wooden pen away before I got started, and then I had to write several letters before I got what I wanted to say on to paper. This is the letter I eventually wrote:

Dear Sir,

    I have just taken a house that used to belong to you. In one bedroom I found some furniture and quite a lot of it was ugly. The chairs were nice, and I've only polished them, but the clock is white now and has a cupid and the beginning of another on it. I've painted some things blue and others are pickled. I thought all those things had been left behind because someone didn't want them any more, and I didn't mean to steal them or damage other people's property. I am sorry.

    I am writing to tell you this so that you won't be shocked when the van arrives with your furniture looking strange.

Yours faithfully,
C.S.

I took the letter to the agents' and asked them to forward it for me. Then I felt a bit better in my mind and went to the house and painted the kitchen. I didn't go near the furniture; fortunately it was all in one room so I could escape from it fairly easily.

Mr Fox turned up in the afternoon. He shouted at the deserters for a bit, then took Jenny and me for a drive in his car. We couldn't go far because he had hardly any petrol; but after stopping at various shops and garages he managed to get some sugar and tinned salmon (Grade I), which he changed for petrol coupons. In one of the garages we saw an old bicycle for sale: it was a lady's one, very heavy and black-looking. I said, 'I wish I had that bicycle' almost without thinking, and the next thing I knew it was being tied to the back of the car. Mr Fox loved doing things like that to give you unexpected surprises. I wasn't really sure if I wanted a bicycle, but when we got home I tried riding it up and down the road and it was rather fun. It didn't have any brakes: you just had to back-pedal.

The next day I took Jenny to school on it; we had to go through the back streets because you were not allowed to take people on the back of your bicycle. I had to tie Scarebones to the handlebars and let him come, too, because he howled so much when he was left behind. It was all rather dangerous because I kept forgetting about the back-pedalling and Scarebones would get in the way.

I went to the new house with lots of instructions from Mr Fox for the workmen. It was difficult to remember all the things he told me because he used to shout them just as he was going. 'Tell the men to get some breeze-slabs – and they are to tie the ballcock down! Get a black-market sink from the back of Newton's – and you'd better order some sand! Send Jim out for some cold-water washers – and Ginger is to wipe all the joints!' He would shout all this as the car engine was running, and before I could ask him any details he was gone.

I told the men all the things I could remember and went to the kitchen to get on with my painting. Although it was only ten o'clock, the workmen had already had one meal of buns and tea, and dirty mugs and half-eaten cakes were arranged on the mantelpiece. I tidied it all up and longed for the day when I could have the house to myself and it would be all clean and tidy; there seemed to be workmen's coats everywhere, hanging from all the door knobs; and battered newspaper parcels and awful pointed shoes were in the cupboards. I attacked my painting with a brush so loaded with paint it ran down the door and on to the floor. It was quite good lino someone had left behind, and I had to get the paint up with my hankie because that was all I could find.

While I was rubbing the floor in front of the door it suddenly opened and a great mess of paint went on my forehead. I shouted, 'Damn you! Can't you be more careful?' But when I looked up it wasn't one of the workmen at all. It was a rather grave-faced man in a dark suit. He was very thin and his nose was large and haughty and I thought he resembled a raven: he was too tidy for a crow. He said, 'I'm sorry about the paint,' and I got up and was going to wipe it off with my hankie but he said, 'You can't use that dirty rag – I'll get it off with mine. Have you any turps?' I produced the turps, which was in a gin-bottle and he carefully wiped my forehead and I felt rather small.

When he had finished he said in an abrupt voice: 'I've come to see what you've done to my furniture,' and I became almost a dwarf. I didn't say anything: just led the way upstairs. It was all in a little white room which made the stripped cupboards look even more ghostlike and the blue things seem awfully bright. He brought out a pair of horn-rimmed spectacles and put them on and looked more like a grave raven than ever. He peered about; then he picked up the half-painted clock and looked at it in a most worried way. Then he said, 'Ha! So this is what you have done to my furniture. Do you think it's an improvement?' I mumbled, 'Yes, I know it is. You should be grateful to have all those improvements to your things.' I thought: 'Now he will be really angry; but however angry he is I shall be even more angry although he is in the right.' His face suddenly began to smile, which completely changed it. It lit up in such a way he became one of the most handsome men I'd ever seen. But it only lasted a second and he became all grave again and I almost thought I must have imagined that change. He said, 'I think you are quite right. You have improved all this old junk immensely, but I don't want it; do keep it if it's any use to you. Goodbye – don't bother to see me out. By the way, I would like to see that clock some time when it's finished.'

He had gone before I could thank him or say anything. I heard a car door slam and went to the window, but he had gone.

CHAPTER FOURTEEN

I suddenly began to feel awfully happy. When I rode about on my heavy bicycle it seemed as if I was flying and I went down the hills without back-pedalling. I enjoyed all kinds of things I'd never noticed before – people, for instance. I'd never cared about them much, but they really were rather nice. Often I'd stood in a street looking at them and thought how ugly they were; if only the street became filled with squirrels and bears and deer and foxes, how different it would look! How could people think they were lords of creation when they were so hideous and miserable and wherever they went they made ugliness and called it 'progress' and 'civilization'? Now I began to notice how kind some people looked and how interesting others were, and some were so good-looking it was a pleasure to see them and watch them moving. I thought perhaps people are an acquired taste like olives.

I enjoyed digging the garden of the new house and

making curtains out of some unrationed material I managed to find; but most of all I enjoyed painting the clock and spent hours over it. Although I was happy, sometimes there was a kind of lump in my chest that stopped me feeling hungry. I re-read all my books and they seemed to have a new meaning for me although I'd read them dozens of times before. Everything seemed to have changed.

A few days before I was due to move, Joseph Weis came to call, and he wore a white carnation in his coat and an even larger and more stripey bow-tie than he had worn before. He was in a very gay mood, but I was nervous because I knew Mr Fox was due to come any minute and I didn't think he would like Joseph very much; also I didn't want him to hear Oliver was dead. I quickly made some tea and explained that he couldn't stay long because I was in the middle of packing, and of course he said he would help me and started heaping things up in a gay and sprightly way. They were all things that were not meant to go together and he was making the most frightful confusion. Eventually I managed to make him sit down and have tea. Jenny thought he was frightfully funny and kept having fits of giggles. When I told him I was going to live in a house with only Jenny, he suggested coming to live with me as a lodger; he got awfully excited by the idea and said he had lots of Czech friends who would love to come, too. We could all live together and be a community. I didn't want to hurt the poor little man's feelings and was wondering how to let him down gently when Mr Fox burst into the room. I could tell he was in one of his bad moods because his ears were sticking out and his lip was all pulled down. He gave our tea-party a furious glance and said, 'When you have time to spare I should like to speak to you.' I asked if he would like some tea and he said, 'No,' but sat down at the table with his legs in everyone's way and tilted his chair back. I introduced him to Joseph Weis and he just nodded his head and said, 'If you have time to waste over tea-parties I haven't. You should be at the house checking that the men don't leave before time; it isn't your money they waste, but mine.' He got up and kicked the table and left the room.

Joseph Weis looked scared, then gave a little giggle and said, 'I hope that angry gentleman isn't your new husband.' I told him he wasn't a husband – just a friend who was a bit eccentric. The eccentric friend opened the door again and shouted, 'Why didn't you tell me the woman on the top floor had a leaking waste-pipe? Whenever I come to this house something is wrong. There you sit giving tea-parties while all the ceilings are being ruined.' I told Joseph he must go and he began to look angry, too, and all his gay air had gone. He picked up his stick and dirty yellow gloves, but couldn't find his hat and gave a scared look at Mr Fox, who stood holding the door-handle. Suddenly he pounced on the unfortunate hat, which had rolled under the table, and banged it on Weis's head and said, 'There's your hat and there is the door!' And out he went after giving me one reproachful glance. Mr Fox slammed the door after him and the poor little man was gone.

Mr Fox was in disgrace after that, and we quarrelled; but he came back the next day and said he had a surprise for me. I tried to be haughty at first, but I do love surprises so much I wasn't haughty very long. He took me out to the car and we drove to the new house and went into the garden. It looked just the same as usual for a moment; then I noticed three matronly brown hens were scratching and clucking away on my newly-sown lawn. He had fixed up a home for them in the little shed and there were some boxes with hay for them to put eggs in. In one box there were three beautiful eggs, only they were white. I picked them up with awe, then had another look and saw they were made of China. We both laughed and Mr Fox was forgiven, and I didn't like to tell him I'd planted a lawn and the hens were stuffing away on the seed. In any case, hens were much better than a lawn.

At last we moved and Jenny and I had the whole house to ourselves except for Scarebones and Mr Fox at weekends and odd days. It was a rest to be away from the tenants and their quarrels and fish, although they often 'phoned. Mr Fox said they had got to have my number in case something drastic happened to the house and they wanted me in a hurry; but it was usually the widow complaining because the Austrians had slammed their door as she was passing, or the Austrians complaining because the widow crept about and listened at their door. I quite dreaded collecting the rents.

We bought some more grand pianos; at one time we had twelve in the house at once. I didn't know how to explain the presence of so many pianos: you couldn't escape them because there were two in the hall lying on their sides and five in the drawing-room, and none of the bedroom doors would shut because they were so full of pianos. When people came to buy them I had to pretend they were unwanted gifts. We only bought one bad piano, and it had a cracked frame and we had to pay some moving men to move it into an empty house to get rid of it. The people who owned the house must have been surprised when they found it there.

Spring came and there was blossom on the trees in the garden; the hens couldn't reach it so it looked perfectly beautiful. The hens ate everything they could reach, which was unfortunate because the garden would have been rather charming if it hadn't been for them. They made up for the destruction they caused by laying heaps of eggs, and they had very nice natures. Eventually I had three cocks and six hens, and when I called, 'Come on, all my fine cocks,' the cocks came rushing to the kitchen window; and if I called, 'Come, my fine hens,' the hens would come tripping to me. Which shows how intelligent they were.

One afternoon the man whose furniture I'd taken called. I had thought about him a lot, and when I went to the door and saw who was there I was glad I was wearing an almost new frock and had plenty of powder and lipstick on my face instead of house paint. He still looked like a raven, but not such a grave one. He said he was just passing and had wondered if I had ever finished painting the clock. I showed him how beautiful it had become – I almost forgot I had painted it myself, and he must have thought me rather boastful. It was teatime so I asked him to stay, and he did. While I was making the tea he went into the garden and found Jenny up a tree. I had quite forgotten all about her and couldn't help wishing she had stayed in her tree until he had gone. Now he would think I was a married woman with a husband coming home any minute. He didn't go away and we talked a lot, and he had such a terribly nice voice. He told me he was a doctor and had a practice in Hampstead, where he lived with his mother. He had a way of talking most seriously, then suddenly his face would light up and it was difficult to know whether he was joking or really meant what he was saying.

When we had nearly finished tea, I suddenly realized I didn't even know his name. In my mind he had always been 'Mr Raven' – I suppose because he resembled one; but actually he was called Dark – Mervyn Dark. He said he knew my name because the agents had told him I was called Mrs Fox. This embarrassed me rather and I told him my real name and said the agents must have made a mistake. I could see Jenny was bursting to say I was called Mrs Fox sometimes and the tenants always called me by that name, so I made a great stir and started to play with Scarebones, who had been quite happily asleep under the table. Then Mervyn said it was time to go and I was glad because I had become afraid Mr Fox would come and be rude. I had been fortunate so far: the house wasn't even stiff with pianos. Before Mervyn left it was arranged I would have lunch with him one day the following week; then he had gone, and it was such a relief he hadn't met Mr Fox. I thought maybe I had better tell him about Mr Fox when we were having lunch – after we had had the sherry, perhaps.

CHAPTER FIFTEEN

Next week came and at last it was the day I was going to have lunch with Mervyn Dark. I went through my rather shabby clothes very carefully and chose a black frock made of fine wool and trimmed with hand-made Spanish lace. I used to wear it at cocktail parties before the war and the lace was really a bit fussy for lunch, but I hoped Mervyn wouldn't notice little things like that. I brushed the dress very carefully and polished a pair of navy court shoes with black polish so that they would match.

I had arranged with the charwoman who cleaned the houses that she would fetch Jenny from school and give her lunch, so I lingered over my dressing and tried my hair several different ways and experimented with various lipsticks; but whatever I did with my face in the way of putting on too much make-up or too little, it still looked at its best. I had noticed just lately it had been improving enormously although I was almost thirty, and I had always expected to grow hideous about that time.

I left the house and the spring sun was warm and all the bottles in a milk-cart that was passing rattled about in a dancing way. The No. 14 'bus I caught in the Fulham Road had been newly painted and the 'bus girl sang to herself in a dreamy manner as she stood on her platform. It was one of those racing, rocking 'buses and we arrived in Piccadilly much too soon; so I crossed the road and looked in a bookshop window. Then, although I only had about half a crown in my bag, I couldn't resist entering the shop and opening a few books. Suddenly it was one o'clock and I should have been at the restaurant. I crossed the road and looked for Stratton Street, but couldn't find it. Someone told me where it was, but when I got there the restaurant I was looking for didn't seem to be there because part of it had been boarded up due to air-raid damage. I was only a quarter of an hour late when I eventually did enter the restaurant, but I could see Mervyn was rather annoyed with me as we walked towards each other over the pink carpet with its design of white cocks. After we had had a drink at the bar he became more human; but I thought maybe I wouldn't tell him about Mr Fox after all.

We had a lovely lunch and he quite forgot about me keeping him waiting, and I really felt so happy. He told me about his life and how he had been invalided out of the army because of some germ he had caught in the East, and he talked about his childhood in the house where I was now living, and it seemed as if I'd known him for years. When we reached the coffee stage he started asking me questions, and I was glad I could say I was a widow; and I could see he was glad I was one, too; but he asked lots of other questions, too, and perhaps it was all the wine we had drunk or else my tongue just ran away with me, but I started to tell him much too much. I could see he was most sympathetic at first and that encouraged me, and it was all going beautifully until I came to Mr Fox. I didn't notice anything at first and told him about Mr Fox going to prison instead of paying his rates, and about the rent collector and how he used to have to play cards with the apprentice to get his salary back. I told him about faked cars and faked references, and the queer deserters who did black-market building, and about the pianos, too. Then I remembered all the lovely food Mr Fox used to get and how whenever I opened my cupboard tins of treacle and meat fell out, and how we used to exchange it for petrol. I would have gone on telling him lots more horrors, but I suddenly noticed his face was looking terribly grim, much sterner than usual. I knew he was shocked to the marrow. I stopped talking and a black silence came between us. Presently he asked a few questions in a very hurt sort of voice, and I answered them all truthfully because I thought it better for him to know all the bad things and get them over. There seemed to be no more to say after that, so he signalled a waiter for his bill and we left soon after. He did offer to drive me home in his car, but I could see he wanted to get rid of me so refused. I walked away while he was still messing about with the self-starter, and I could feel him looking after me. Although I was so miserable I hoped the seams in my stockings were straight, but expect they were crooked. When I reached Piccadilly everyone looked so cheerful in the sun and I rather hated them, but not so much as I hated myself. I waited in a queue for a 'bus and went home.

In the days that followed I felt almost as depressed as when we lived at Straws. Mervyn Dark did not write or 'phone, but I hadn't really expected him to. Mr Fox must have heard that I had been out to lunch; most likely the charwoman had told him. He suddenly said he was giving up his room and was coming to live with me all the time. I knew it would be like living at Straws all over again, and everything seemed hopeless. All the seeds I had planted in the garden were coming up beautifully and the hens were laying heaps of eggs, but I took no pleasure in these things now. I could hardly bear to enter the little shed where the hens lived because Mervyn had told me it used to be his toolshed when he was a little boy and he did carpentry there. On the walls there were some rough homemade shelves which he must have fixed, and there was a very ragged blueprint nailed to the door, and when I looked carefully I could see it had a model ship on it. All these things made me sad.

Mr Fox came to live in the house and the wireless was on all the time he was home, and he used to get impatient with me because I couldn't see jokes and hated funny men that shouted. We had trouble about me forgetting all the things he shouted just as he was leaving the house at about seven in the morning. I couldn't remember where I was to go to in Camden Town to get black-market linseed-oil, or which sale-room was selling seven grandfather clocks. Pianos had become rather difficult to find because lots of other people had started selling them, too. In fact, when we did buy and advertise a piano, a number of dealers would turn up and would go away without looking at the piano when they recognized me on the doorstep. But eventually pianos became so scarce that dealers bought them from each other, and they went round and round to different dealers, getting more expensive all the time. Grandfather clocks didn't sell very well, and it was awful having six or seven in the house all chiming away at various times.

People were more interested in D-Day than grand-father clocks. In shops they were always pretending they knew when D-Day was coming, and middle-aged men who may at one time have been in the Civil Service used to hint that they were the only men in England, except perhaps Churchill, who knew the D-Day secrets. They would say, 'Well, I can tell you it won't be this week, and it won't be on Sunday; it may be on a Wednesday but, on the other hand, it may not. I could tell you the exact day, of course, but I dare not do such a thing.' I tried to avoid any man who looked as if he might have something like that to say, but they took a lot of avoiding.

Then another horror happened. Mr Fox was put on night duty, and it was awful. He used to arrive back so grumpy just as I was getting up in the morning, and he would want a kind of supper instead of breakfast; then he would go to bed and I had to be very quiet. But the telephone wasn't. As soon as he went to sleep it would start and often it was for me – something quite harmless like some little girl's mother asking Jenny to tea. The 'phone was by his bed and he would yell down it in a frightful way. I wanted to leave the receiver off, but he wouldn't have that in case it was someone wanting to buy a grand-father clock. When the telephone wasn't ringing it was the doorbell, and when that went Scarebones would start to bark wildly, and although I hit him he went on doing it, and sometimes I thought Nathaniel Gubbins had very sound ideas about dogs. But the hens made even more noise than Scarebones: they were always laying eggs because it was spring, and every time they did it they would start cackling away and wouldn't stop. Mr Fox would shout from his bed, 'For Christ's sake shut those hens up!' and I would try prodding them, or even chasing them until they were short of breath; but they went on making that awful noise. Once I became so desperate I held a hen's beak shut and she went dreadfully red in the face and I felt cruel. The cocks had usually got their crowing over by the time he returned.

After a month of night duty Mr Fox changed over to day work and life became easier and he suddenly became very gay. Nearly every week we went to a theatre and we had dinner in a different restaurant each time. We always chose ones we had never been to before so we never knew what kind of dinner we were up against, but that made it more amusing, and often in the cheaper places we had really marvellous food. Later on something happened that made me very glad we had had this carefree time together. It wasn't quite carefree for me really because I was still feeling rather crushed about Mervyn and felt angry with myself for minding so much; but the desperate sadness which had come over me after that ghastly lunch was beginning to lift. Summer was just beginning and there had been no air raids for some time, and there seemed to be a hopeful atmosphere everywhere and it made me hopeful, too.

Then, when people weren't talking quite so much about D-Day it came, and everyone was as excited as if the war was really over. Out came the flags and it became almost an unofficial holiday. Mr Fox made it one, anyway. We drove about the London streets and he suddenly had the idea of buying me a complete new outfit of clothes. I told him I'd spent all my coupons on Jenny's school uniform and he looked quite surprised and said, 'Coupons? Why didn't you say you were short of them? I've got hundreds.' And out of his wallet came five books, all with different names on the cover. I knew Mervyn Dark would think I was wicked to take them, but I did, and I spent forty pounds that came out of Mr Fox's wallet as well. As I bought my ill-gotten clothes I thought, 'I wish you could see how wicked I'm being, Mervyn; it would serve you right for being such a prig.' But I knew nothing I did mattered to him any more; he just thought I was hopeless.

Mr Fox was in a spending mood, so we went to a toy-shop in Regent Street and bought the most spectacular toy in the shop – a large model barrel-organ which played six different tunes. It really was beautiful and it made Jenny so happy she would play with it for hours, and the music was that heavenly tinkly kind that comes out of musical boxes.

I changed into all my new clothes, but I didn't really want to go out on D-Day evening because I didn't like leaving Jenny. I was afraid there would be an enormous air raid and perhaps even gas. I could tell Mr Fox was disappointed, so we compromised and went to a restaurant in the Brompton Road so that we could get home quickly if there was an air-raid warning. There wasn't one and I felt I had been rather silly and nervous and spoilt Mr Fox's evening after he had been so kind and given me such beautiful clothes and Jenny her lovely barrel-organ. We walked home after dinner, and although there was a full moon it was dark and rather cold, and I suddenly felt sad.

The following day I managed to buy two Broad-wood pianos quite cheap in a Knightsbridge sale-room, and I was glad because I felt a bit guilty letting Mr Fox spend so much money on me. But as soon as he had any spare money he couldn't help spending it; if I hadn't had it he would have wasted it on something else. Sometimes he would go to a sale to buy a grandfather clock and come back with three cut-glass rose-bowls and a rubber dinghy. Every time he passed a jeweller's window he had to stop. It was a wonder he wasn't a burglar because he admired jewellery and things that glittered so much. If I had encouraged him he would have given me masses of it, but I didn't like modern jewellery much, and in any case it would have had to spend most of its life in a pawnshop, because sometimes Mr Fox was stiff with money and other times it had all gone. But while it lasted he wasted it with great enjoyment, although of course it wasn't wasted if it gave him so much pleasure.

Everyone was talking about the Second Front, and all the bores who used to pretend they knew when it was coming said, 'Ah! what did I tell you? I knew D-Day would be on a Tuesday in June,' and they would shut their eyes in a smug way as they talked. I have often noticed bores do this, maybe so that they can't see people's impatient faces.

Days passed and there weren't any dreadful air raids: all that happened was a thunderstorm on Sunday evening while we were cleaning the pianos, which were really in very good condition except that some rods that should have been fixed to the pedals of one of the pianos were missing. But Mr Fox soon fixed them with some electric light flex. He cleaned the insides of the pianos and I polished the outside, and except for all the carving on the legs they looked almost like new when we had finished. Jenny played her barrel-organ to us while we worked, and the thunder rumbled away in the background.

CHAPTER SIXTEEN

All Wednesday night there were strange noises. It seemed to be a never-ending air raid, and even when morning came there was no All Clear, and the strange noises and gunfire still went on. I didn't let Jenny go to school. The sun came out very bright and I went into the garden and looked up into the sky, but all I could see was blue, until some gunfire came and made little puffs of cotton-wool, which melted away. And then I thought I saw a small 'plane flying very straight with fire and smoke coming out of its tail; but afterwards I thought maybe it was a figment of my imagination. All day there were crashes and bangs, and I felt lonely and worried until Mr Fox returned. He told me the things that were cracking about the sky were pilotless 'planes that the Germans were sending over; they were an awful kind of secret weapon. He thought I should send Jenny out of London, but I didn't know where to send her.

People began to call the pilotless 'planes 'flying

bombs', which didn't sound so frightening. It was horrible to wake up in the night and hear one coming nearer and making the most dreadful noise as it came; then the noise would suddenly stop and I would think, 'This is the end,' and put my pillow on my head. There would be the most frightful crash and the doors often burst open; but it wasn't the end after all. The people next door went away, and they said if I would look after their Pekingese they would give me a pair of real linen sheets. I would have looked after the dog for nothing but was glad to have the sheets because we were so short of them, and often the laundry didn't return for weeks. Everyone seemed to be leaving London, and suddenly there were no children in the streets again. Jenny's school was badly damaged and had to close. One of the mothers came to see me and offered to take Jenny into the country with her child. I hardly knew the woman and was quite overcome with her kindness, and I promised I would go and look at her house every day and let her know if it was damaged. I was glad to do something in return.

As soon as I knew Jenny was safe I didn't mind the flying bombs so much; but Scarebones and the Peek were terrified of them, and every time they heard one coming they dived under my bed and made the most frightful scrabbling noises, which always woke me up and made me hear every flying bomb for miles around which I might have missed if it hadn't been for them.

The weather became warm and delightful, and I

began to enjoy an almost empty London. Shopping
became almost a pleasure and sometimes we would go
to a theatre and there would be hardly anyone there;
and it was the same in restaurants. Often in the
evening we would take the dogs for a walk in Hyde
Park and it would be deserted and lovely. Once when
we were walking home a flying bomb stopped right
over our heads, and as we turned and ran in the
opposite direction a great explosion came and then an
enormous amount of dust. The dogs were more upset
than we were. Although covered in dirt we were quite
unhurt, but what amazed us was how quickly the
ARP people arrived and roped off the site where the
bomb had fallen. No one was hurt because the houses
were already almost wrecked from a previous bomb.
As we returned home through the back streets we
passed a derelict police-station which Mr Fox became
most interested in because he thought it could be
converted into flats. He was so enthusiastic that we
had to climb all over it in the half light. He said he
would buy it and call it Peel House, but fortunately
the next day he changed his mind.

I had a dear little letter from Jenny, telling me she
had been down the dell and caught a hedgehog which
she fed on bread and milk. She asked me to visit her.
So I went into the country for the day and it was a
relief to get away from bombs; but I worried about
the house all the time in case something awful happened while I was away. I felt it was more likely to
happen if I wasn't there to will the bombs away. I

took some food down with me because I didn't want to be a bother to the people she was staying with. We went for a picnic by a stream, and paddled, and made little harbours and dams, and had the nicest day together we had had for a long time.

London looked very dirty and battered when I returned, but the house was still standing. To my dismay the 'phone rang as soon as I entered the house, and it was someone wanting to buy a piano – the advertisements had come out in one of the papers. In spite of air raids people still seemed to want pianos, and the 'phone hardly stopped ringing all the evening. Mr Fox came home and helped me cope with it, and before we went to bed we had sold both the pianos and promised to deliver them the next day. We wanted to get them out of the house so that if they were bombed it wouldn't be our funeral.

The following morning I got up from my uncomfortable bed in the basement passage and discovered Mr Fox had already left his hideout under the stairs and had gone for a walk with the dogs. I must have forgotten to shut the poultry in their little shed, because there they were, all sitting on the kitchen window-sill waiting for their breakfast. Mr Fox had left a kettle boiling, so I mixed their Ballancer meal and left it to cool while I prepared our breakfast. It was rather a black-market meal as usual – plenty of butter and eggs and bacon. I had been feeling a bit self-conscious about our food lately. Everything was ready when Mr Fox returned. He was in a gay mood and was full of some plan he had just thought of – something to do with making his factory think he was redundant so that he could leave and be free.

We sat down at the breakfast-table and I was just pouring out the coffee when I saw all the hens' sad faces looking through the window. They had a kind of disappointed look, so I remembered their cooling food and ran out with it. I usually fed them at the bottom of the garden because they made such a mess. I went down the garden holding the bowl and calling, 'Come on, all my fine cocks. Come on, my fine hens!' And they raced after me and the dogs came, too, and stole lumps of Ballancer meal that they wouldn't have touched with a barge pole if I'd put it on their own plates.

I heard a beastly flying bomb coming, and the dogs stopped stealing and came and sat shivering by me. It became so loud and near I became afraid, too, and wanted to hurry back to the house, only somehow I couldn't move. I thought I heard Mr Fox call, but there was so much noise I wasn't sure. I thought, 'As long as I hear that noise it won't fall here.' Then I saw it making straight for me, and it came so low over the house that slates fell off as it passed. I imagined it had a dreadful wicked face, but I couldn't move and then a great draught came. I went up into the air with the hens; we went in a kind of whirlwind; the dogs seemed to be sucked right away. Suddenly I found myself on the ground and my elbows hurt rather. The hens were all coming down, too, and there was a great noise of falling glass and slates and pieces of twisted metal like swords were flying around. I got to my feet and pulled my housecoat round me, but the seams had mostly come undone. Where the garden wall had been there was a heap of broken stones and twisted metal: it looked about a hundred years old, not shining new metal. I turned towards the house and as I did so an All Clear went, and I heard myself muttering, 'You damn fools, it isn't clear here.'

The poor house! The roof had almost gone and some of the chimney pots; the windows were sad, blind holes, and great cracks and splits had come in the walls. I couldn't bear to go in. I just stood muttering through my hands, which for some reason I held over my mouth. I didn't have to open the back door because it had gone, and I walked down the passage I had been sleeping in. But my bed was up-ended and had gone through the drawing-room floor. I went into the room that used to be a dining-room. It wouldn't be one any more: most of the drawing-room had fallen into it and all the doors had gone. I looked for Mr Fox and he wasn't there at first, but afterwards I saw him by the window. I found myself saying out loud, 'You must get used to things like this,' over and over again. He was lying rather twisted, so I tried to make him more comfortable. There was hardly any blood and he didn't look dreadful. His eyes were open and he looked kind of jaunty, as he often did; but I knew he was dead. He must have gone to the window to call me. That was the thing they kept telling you not to do – to go by windows.

Some men started to shout upstairs, but I didn't take any notice, and after they had banged about quite a lot they came down to the basement. They took me away from Mr Fox and someone tried to wrap a blanket round me and I became most indignant, I don't know why.

Quite soon they took Mr Fox away and they wanted to take me to a rest centre, but I said I'd rather stay where I was. People kept coming and being kind and wanting me to do things I didn't want to do; and I thought, 'If I dress and look more normal they won't interfere so much.' I went upstairs and there was rubble everywhere, and on the pianos we had sold as well. I knew Mr Fox would want me to clear them before I did anything, and it seemed almost as if he was there; so I didn't feel so alone.

When I was dressed I went to find the dogs, and I kept asking the awful people who had come to gape if they had seen them; but they seemed to have vanished. No one had seen them. The hens were pecking away in the garden; they were very dusty but seemed unharmed; but only one cock had survived and it had a queer leg now. I could never say, 'Come on, all my fine cocks' any more. An awful dirty little object came creeping along the ground and it was the poor little Peek. Her eyes were filled with dirt, but otherwise she was quite unharmed. To my great joy Scarebones returned about an hour later and I gave them a large tin of Spam to eat. I didn't want to have any more black-market food because I felt it might be unlucky. I could still see the butter all cut to pieces by glass and the plates of bacon with a ceiling on top, and the kitchen cupboard that used to be so full was in a dreadful state.

Some ARP men came and said it was no good clearing the house because it was in too bad a state to be lived in any more; but they did help me clean the pianos and I managed to get them away in a lorry, and you could hardly tell they had been in a wrecked house. Anyway, the people who bought them didn't complain.

I worked so hard the next few days and it almost seemed as if Mr Fox was there helping me and telling me what to do. I don't think I would have been able to get through it if it hadn't been for that feeling. It was only afterwards, when I had moved into a tiny flat with my few belongings, that I really began to realize that he wasn't there any more.

CHAPTER SEVENTEEN

The tiny flat was in a basement just off the Fulham Road, quite near the hospitals. I was able to salvage enough furniture to make it fairly comfortable. At first I didn't care how it looked, because I felt so depressed, lonely and hopeless; but after a few weeks I couldn't stand the wallpaper any longer and covered it with distemper; and then I made curtains and it began to look quite attractive.

After I'd been there about a month there were not many bombs getting through to London, so the people who had been looking after Jenny returned and, of course, brought her back with them. To begin with there was rather an upset because all her toys were gone, even the barrel-organ. I had to comb the shops to try and find a few things that were not too expensive, and it was rather a sad little collection I managed to get together eventually.

I still received a small income from the house we bought with our war-damage money. The house next door I gave to Mr Fox's mother because it didn't really belong to me. But I kept the money from the pianos and I had several hundred pounds owing to me for war-damage compensation, so I could manage fairly well. I did find food a problem, though. I had forgotten how small war-time rations were. For a time there were still eggs from the hens. After being bombed they seemed to lay much better and I kept discovering nests of eggs all over the garden. Then the hens started to die, one by one, and they took days to do it. There seemed to be half-dead hens everywhere and I hadn't the heart to kill them outright. They worried me a lot, and I had to keep holding up their nearly dead necks and giving them water out of an eggcup. They became awfully smelly, too: it quite put me off eggs.

When all the hens had died and I hadn't got them to worry about any more, I thought it would be a good idea to take a holiday, and I decided on Cornwall.

We went to a village near St Agnes and stayed in a wooden cottage right on a lonely beach. There was usually a great wind and at night it seemed as if the cottage would blow away. Once the gale was so fierce it made an enormous froth over the sea, and soon it became piled up all over the beach; and the cottage was half buried, too. We would dash out into the storm and hold on to rocks or we would have been blow away. Our faces and clothes became covered in froth and sand, and our ears would be filled with the savage wind. When the tide went out after a storm we used to explore the caves, which became filled with strange things. Once Jenny found a battered rag doll with seaweed in her hair. She called her 'Found Drowned'. Often we discovered corks from fishermen's nets and sometimes glass balls, which we loved. One evening when I was alone on the beach a wave washed up three glass balls, and there they were, all wet and shining, at my feet. It seemed like a beautiful dream. Sometimes in the evening a seal would swim across the bay. It was the kind of place where things like that would happen.

I never bought a newspaper all the time I was in Cornwall and sometimes I would think, 'Perhaps the war is over and I don't know.' Occasionally people would come on our beach and try and talk to me. Once they told me the Germans were sending over a new kind of secret weapon called a 'V 2' that just came without making any noise and that was the end of you. But the war seemed so far away, and at night I would sit by my fire of bleached wood washed up from the sea and I would feel safe and strangely contented.

The days went so quickly, and soon it was time to return to London and my sad little garden with its dirty brick walls. We said goodbye to the derelict tin mines with their bleak, empty windows overlooking the sea, and we went to the wall where lizards darted when the sun shone, and the dell near the cottage where the large grass snakes were. We explored the long echoing caves for the last time, and gazed into clear rock pools which seemed like another world.

We came home looking very brown: even the brown parts of Scarebones seemed to have turned darker. I had dreaded returning, but really it wasn't so bad as I expected. I was quite glad to see the flat again, and it wasn't so dreary as I had remembered it in Cornwall; and the garden had possibilities, too: I went out there on my first morning home and resolved to limewash the dark walls and get rid of the clinkers and ivy and incidentally the woodlice and spiders.

I sat on a thing that was meant to be a rockery and opened some of the letters that I had found piled up on the doormat in the hall. On closer inspection they mostly proved to be bills or complaints from the tenants; but there was one real letter and I knew who it was from before I read it. It was from Mervyn. After all these months he had written. His letter would have meant so much to me a few weeks ago: a letter so filled with love and kindness and, for some reason, reproach for himself. He had been trying to trace us for weeks, ever since he had heard of the dreadful thing that had happened, and he wanted to marry me and look after Jenny and me with the greatest care in the world. Perhaps it was pity that had made him write that. The letter was so good and kind that I felt I wanted to cry; but I didn't love him any more. So much had happened lately he had been pushed out of my mind. He was just a good, kind man

I had once known, and perhaps he really was rather a prig. I didn't care about the little boy who had put up the crooked shelves in the henhouse: he was just any boy. For a few moments I tried to imagine how it would be if I was married to Mervyn, but it seemed quite unreal. I could only think of stupid things. Most likely he would be upset because I never remembered to put the top back on the toothpaste, and there would be trouble because I usually mended socks with contrasting wool because it wasn't so boring darning them like that. He was stern, too, and often grave. Perhaps his mother would expect to live with us, and I had seen a photograph of her showing her bottom teeth. People who show their bottom teeth are always bad-tempered. No, the time for Mervyn Dark was past. Maybe I would fall in love with someone else and most likely I'd get married, but not yet. I wasn't ready to meet people yet. I had a sort of feeling that if I kept very calm and quiet a protective cover would come and dim my memory. I could get out of the darkness better alone.

Already I felt much better about Mr Fox. I had been quite haunted by the thought of him in his lonely grave – most probably going mouldy by now, with his eyes that had been so wide open all glazed. I remembered how unkind I'd been at Straws, so unsympathetic and hard; I wouldn't even give the poor man bread-pudding when he asked for it. Things like that used to keep coming to my mind, and his rather surprised dead face in the room that wouldn't be a dining-room any more. I used to try to push these thoughts away, but they would keep coming. Then in Cornwall they didn't come so much; I began to feel the real Mr Fox wasn't in his grave at all. He was most likely charging about somewhere, perhaps in another world, where he would break every rule and stir things up; and perhaps Tantivy would be at his heels. If he had managed to get to purgatory or somewhere like that he would soon make a short circuit to heaven, and once there he would obtain the biggest and best harp, simply stiff with real gold leaf. Maybe he would do a little business with second-hand harps. He would never be content to sit on a cloud, at least not for long. I could imagine deserter angels of darkness would come and spray his cloud a different colour every day, and he would let off part of it as a self-contained flat. I felt quite sure he had an interesting future in front of him wherever he was, and he would never for a moment waste time going mouldy in a grave.

I began to feel quite happy about Mr Fox as I sat on the rockery that was made of clinkers, and I couldn't see the black garden walls any more. I was suddenly filled with hope. I'd always felt the future held wonderful things for me. I'd never quite caught up with it, but quite soon I would. I felt sure I hadn't long to wait.

ALSO BY

BARBARA COMYNS

from turnpike books

THE HOUSE OF DOLLS

"A magical novel… essential reading for anyone who appreciates good fiction." — *Independent*

"A magical novel… essential reading for anyone who appreciates good fiction." – *Independent*

Evelyn and Berti are divorcees, addicted to tight trousers and drink, surviving on small annuities and they do not get on well together.

Though well past their prime, there is an air of breeding about them but something distinctly odd too. They live in a boarding-house in Kensington dreaming of the past, real and imagined, and better days. They are not exactly tarts, but they have established a bordello for elderly gentle people in their living-room and a little makeshift prostitution helps to pay the rent.

The business has its problems: their landlady is a reluctant madam, Ivy is in love with a dentist from Putney, one of their gentlemen suddenly dies. What will become of Evelyn and Berti?